NON-DESTRUCTIVE TESTING OF

STEEL WIRE ROPES

Proceedings of a symposium
London - 6 December 1988

Edited by

AE Potts

Department of Engineering, University of Reading

Symposium organised by the British Institute of Non-Destructive Testing
in co-operation with the University of Reading

The British Institute of Non-Destructive Testing
1 Spencer Parade
Northampton NN1 5AA
Tel: 0604 30124 Telex: 31612 OTSSG Fax: 0604 231489

ISBN 0 903132 17 6

Printed in Great Britain by
Antony Rowe Ltd, Chippenham, Wiltshire

CONTENTS

INTRODUCTION

A.E. POTTS

" As no physician of today would ignore X-ray apparatus, so no engineer who has ropes in his care can afford to neglect modern methods of electromagnetic rope testing"— Harvey and Kruger, 1959.

Despite the existence of practical wire rope NDT systems for over 30 years with extensive operational experience and requirements for its use in various applications in many countries, little use has been made of these techniques within the UK to date. There is very poor awareness within industry, regulatory and certification bodies and standards organisations dealing with ropes as to the capabilities of the available NDT techniques, their use in other parts of the world and the operational and cost benefits from using these devices. What is not recognised is that reliance on the established visual examination techniques and currently recommended discard criteria may be conservative but not necessarily safe. Visual examination of ropes is cumbersome, time consuming, highly subjective and inherently limited. NDT has a proven capability in detecting various types and levels of rope damage easily missed or not apparent to the eye of the rope inspector, and is particularly suited to long lengths of rope which try the concentration of inspectors.

In most applications using ropes, the cost of replacement ropes is usually negligible in comparison with the rest of the equipment or the returns from the operation itself. This tends to colour the attitude of the designers and operators, such that the ropes are often seen as relatively inexpensive consumables and accordingly there is little investment in rope inspection techniques and maintenance procedures. Where a maximum allowable service life for a rope is specified there is even less incentive for operators to consider investing in NDT equipment and in training personnel to use these devices. The cost–benefit case for the use of NDT equipment should consider the cost of plant/ installation down-time for maintenance, inspection and replacement which may be very high or even worse the consequences of rope failure in terms of loss of life and/or equipment. The time savings from using NDT instead of visual examination and the additional information on rope condition it produces can minimize down-time and provides a more rational and reliable basis for determining rope discard.

Department of Engineering, University of Reading,
Whiteknights, P.O.Box 225, Reading, Berkshire, RG6 2AY, UK.

The aim of this symposium was to raise the level of awareness among wire rope users, regulators and certifiers about available NDT techniques for assessing the condition of steel wire ropes in-service. To this end the authors were approached to write papers on particular topics, including:

(i)   the state-of-the art and types of NDT devices currently available;
(ii)   the limitations of conventional visual inspection procedures;
(iii)   the types and sizes of ropes that can be tested and the applications where NDT devices may best be used;
(iv)   the level of acceptance and reliability of these devices in other countries and associated regulations and/or codes of practice;
(v)   cost savings from using NDT devices for inspecting ropes; and,
(vi)   the future developments of NDT devices and techniques.

In addition, a number of manufacturers of electromagnetic NDT equipment were invited to exhibit their products at the symposium. The firms exhibiting included:

(i)   NDT Technologies Inc. from the USA and their UK agent;
(ii)   Rotesco Inc. from Canada with BIRAL their UK agent;
(iii)   WBK-Seilprüfstelle and their agent Dr. Brandt GmbH from Bochum, West Germany; and,
(iv)   Hawker Siddley Dynamics Engineering Ltd who manufacture the British Coal device.

The authors from the University of Mining and Metallurgy, Kraków, and the representatives from the Polish NDT manufacturers, Mera-Ster, were unfortunately unable to attend at the very last moment, although their paper, which describes the Mera-Ster devices and their applications, is included.

In addition to the papers, a comprehensive bibliography on the NDT of steel wire ropes has been compiled and included in these proceedings. The 267 references may be of interest to those attending the symposium wishing to find out more about wire rope NDT techniques and also serve to illustrate the point that there is a large background of experience and knowledge on the subject.

The symposium obviously struck a vein of interest and concern in the industry on the fact that there was a 'full house' at the Institute of Metals and their was vigorous and wide ranging discussions at the end of each paper and in the open discussion session after the final paper, for which most attendees remained to participate in. One positive action which seems to have arisen from these discussions is the future formation of a committee within the British Institute of Non-Destructive Testing to develop some guidelines or a code of practice on the NDT of steel wire ropes.

It is hoped that this symposium achieved what it set out to do and has raised the general level of awareness on this subject within the UK. In all the symposium, which was the first of its kind in the UK, was a success and it is hoped that it will not be the last such gathering.

A REVIEW OF WIRE ROPE NON-DESTRUCTIVE TESTING AND

ITS PRACTICAL APPLICATION

C.H.H.CORDEN

SUMMARY

The paper introduces wire rope non-destructive testing techniques to rope examiners. It concentrates mainly on the magnetic method and indicated how this is used in conjunction with more traditional visual inspection methods. After describing the different types of instrument which have been developed it discusses the practical application of the technique under service conditions. Problems which may be met in the field and some of the limitations are mentioned. The paper includes a general introduction to the analysis of the defect signals from the instruments. Recent developments in instrumentation, and thoughts on possible future ones, are covered together with the author's views on developments on the signal processing side, such as fault density monitors, which have been demonstrated and could be made available to rope examiners.

1. INTRODUCTION

In many rope installations today the nature and complexity of the whole system, the intensity of use, and the need to carry out periodic checks on many different items means that less and less time is available for the inspection and maintenance of the ropes. Many ropes are used in dark and dirty environments, or they can be covered by thick layers of lubricant and dirt; they may be inaccessible for much of the rope path, and they can be hundreds or thousands of metres in length. All these factors make effective visual inspection extremely difficult, tedious and costly.

In the last two decades there have also been many cases where wire ropes have failed in service, or where the deterioration in them has reached a very advanced stage before being detected. Some ropes physically cannot be opened up for a proper internal examination whilst in service because of their actual construction e.g. locked coil ropes, ropes with plastic sleeves etc. Experience has shown

Health & Safety Executive, Research & Laboratory Services Division, Broad Lane, Sheffield, S3 7HQ, UK that in some circumstances in these ropes internal deterioration, such as localised corrosion, can reach the 50% loss in the overall strength of the rope level before the damage produces some external manifestation of its presence.

All these factors have illustrated the need for better methods of inspecting ropes than the traditional visual method used alone. Today for many ropes visual examination is no longer considered adequate and there is a strong case for the wider application of non-destructive testing (NDT) methods.

Records reveal that interest has been shown in the non-destructive testing of wire ropes from the early 1900's. Through the 1920's and 1930's there was a lot of activity, mainly in countries with mining industries, with the main effort concentrated on shaft hoisting ropes. In Europe, Germany and Poland were two of the countries closely associated with this work. The 1950's saw instruments in use in many other countries not only on mining ropes but also on cableways and aerial ropeways. In the UK there are references to the magnetic technique in papers to the Safety in Mines Research Board in the 1920's and 1930's and by the late 1930's several experimental rigs had been built to look at mine hoisting ropes. In general however the UK has been well behind some other countries in the exploitation of NDT for wire ropes, and especially for mine hoisting ropes. Part of the reluctance of the UK coal mining industry to adopt NDT methods for its winding ropes has been due to the very high standards of visual inspection and maintenance which it has been able to sustain, but other factors such as the high proportion of locked-coil winding ropes in use, which are more difficult to examine even by NDT methods, influenced earlier decisions. Today however there is a growing awareness of the advantages of NDT for wire ropes, and with the numbers of commercial instruments increasing, more and more rope users in many industries are investigating the possibilities of using these techniques on their ropes.

2. NDT METHODS FOR WIRE ROPES

Although this symposium concentrates mainly on the magnetic, or electromagnetic as it is sometimes called, method of testing wire ropes a brief mention should be made of some of the alternatives. There are four which in the author's opinion deserve mention, these are, in no special order: Radiography, Acoustic Emission, Ultrasonics, and Dynamic Measurement Techniques.

2.1 Radiography

Radiography as practiced in the NDT examination of metallic components is a well tried and successful method which is also widely used for the examination of pipelines in service. It could be used on individual rope wires but past experience in the UK indicates that it

8

is generally difficult to use on wire ropes. The main difficulty arises from the fact that the rope is made up from many individual wires, in some places with areas of metal-to-metal contact, in other places with metal-to-air or metal-to-lubricant interfaces. The result is that the waves are reflected from a multiplicity of surfaces which produces a blurring effect in which real cracks or wire breaks are generally invisible unless the defect is close to the surface of the rope or strand. Experience on ropes of the locked-coil construction in the UK has shown that generally only defects in the outer two layers of the rope can be located and even then only with difficulty. Though there have been a few cases investigated where massive disruptions in the lay of the internal layers in locked coil ropes have produced tell-tale shadows on the photographs. The technique is not suited to the rapid location of defects in long lengths of rope though there may, with suitable research, be some use for it on certain special ropes after other techniques, such as the magnetic method, have located complex internal defects which need further NDT examination. For wire rope or strand examination the use of the technique on site, rather than under laboratory conditions, raises other safety and practical difficulties.

Radiography might have some application for the examination of rope anchorages on bridge hangers and suspension cables in situations where resin capping materials are beginning to replace zinc or white metal. In these types of anchorages deterioration can occur just within the neck of the socket/anchorage, usually in the outer layers of the cable, either due to wind induced oscillations which lead to fretting between wires, or due to corrosion from water running down the cables. Radiography of wire ropes is a topic which perhaps deserves further research for some special applications.

2.2 Acoustic Emission

Research in the UK at the Department of Materials Science and Metallurgical Engineering at University College Cardiff over a period of seven years, partly sponsored by the HSE, has produced some very valuable data on the application of this technique to wire ropes. One of the outputs from this work was the development of a wire break counter which detects the breakage of individual wires by the pulse of energy which is released. Such an instrument could be very valuable for laboratory fatigue work and a similar device has been used for this purpose by the WBK's Seilprüfstelle in Bochum, Federal Republic of Germany. The technique may also have applications in the field if its long term stability can be guaranteed. Investigations are also known to have been made at several other research establishments in the UK, Europe and the USA. This technique would not be readily applicable to moving ropes but might be further developed for some special applications such as offshore anchor lines. In the UK at the present time some further work is being conducted on this topic at the National Engineering Laboratory (NEL), East Kilbride.

A more detailed paper by N F Casey from NEL on some aspects of this subject is included later in these proceedings.

2.3 Ultrasonics

Ultrasonics do not appear to be of use on moving ropes, or on ropes of great length, but they can be used to check the integrity of individual wires in a rope capping - a critical area where most other NDT techniques cannot be used. To carry out an ultrasonic test the wires must be allowed to protrude from the capping so that an ultrasonic probe can be attached to them. This technique has been used by the WBK's Seilprüfstelle, Bochum, and possibly elsewhere, to examine rope anchorages on bridge hangers and suspension cable To accomplish access to the wire ends normal conical rope sockets with attachment lugs are not used, instead the rope is capped in a conical sleeve which seats in a conical or cylindrical fitting on the bridge deck.

2.4 Dynamic Measurements

Research has shown that certain characteristics of wire ropes, such as stiffness and hysteresis, change as a rope deteriorates. Measuring techniques exploiting various forms of dynamic behaviour could provide information on either of these mechanical indicators. A short introduction to this topic has been published by Chaplin and Potts (1). At this time it is not thought that these techniques have been researched or developed outside the laboratory into commercially available packages suitable for the practicing engineer in the field. By their nature they would look basically at the average condition of the length being tested, though any local defect in this length would obviously have some effect.

2.5 Magnetic/Electromagnetic

This is a successful and well tried method which is now in use in many countries throughout the world. Much of the original development work was done in connection with mining ropes but now the technique is being used much more widely. It can be used on both running and stationary ropes, and it is the only practical method to monitor the condition of long lengths of rope quickly. It cannot however be used to examine the short vulnerable length of a rope close to an end fitting, and it can only be applied to wire ropes, strand and cables made from magnetic materials. It cannot therefore be used for the detection of faults in most stainless steel ropes, copper or aluminium cables, but it can be used to detect defects in any steel armouring around such cables. It can also be used to detect defects in the steel wires of plastic covered ropes.

The rest of this paper concentrates on this technique.

3. MAGNETIC/ELECTROMAGNETIC METHODS

There are basically two methods of magnetic/electromagnetic inspection (1) the so called AC method, and (2) the DC energised magnet or the permanent magnet method. Both methods have been widely used over many years; each has certain advantages and disadvantages relative to the other. These methods have generally proved successful on ropes in most applications. In many cases they are the only NDT methods which can be carried out effectively and efficiently in the field within the available time span for a rope inspection.

Figure 1 illustrates a minor defect which would probably have been impossible to find in a long rope by visual inspection alone but which would have been easily detected by a magnetic NDT instrument even when covered by lubricant and dirt.

3.1 AC Instruments

The majority of the AC wire rope NDT instruments in very simplistic terms work on the transformer principle. There are primary and secondary coils wound round the rope which act as the transformer core so that in effect any significant change in the magnetic characteristics of the core i.e. in the volume of the rope within the region of influence of the coils at any moment, will be reflected in changes of voltage in the secondary turns and phase shift changes between the primary and secondary signals. The magnetic characteristics of the appropriate length of rope are influenced by factors such as wear and corrosion.

AC systems operate both stationary and on moving ropes so locating the positions of indicated defects accurately is relatively easy.

These instruments generally work at relatively low magnetic field strengths and it is therefore necessary to completely demagnetise the rope before any inspection can be made. If this is not done then the results of the tests could be influenced by localised residual magnetism picked up by the rope during its service life e.g. from the effects of the earth's magnetic field.

The AC system generates eddy currents in the wires of the rope as it passes through the insPPument which then oppose the further penetration of the magnetic field deeper into the rope. Locked-coil ropes are particularly affected by these eddy currents and as a result this method has been less successful on this type of rope. Operating frequencies were mostly in the region of 50Hz to 80Hz in the early instruments but later frequencies in the range 10Hz to 20Hz were tried with some success. The chosen operating frequency and the resulting delay in the penetration of the field due to the eddy currents can influence the rope inspection speed. At the lower operating frequencies there is a limitation, for the period of oscillation must be much less than the time required for the sampled portion of the rope to pass through the instrument.

Instruments of this type were very suitable for monitoring changes in the metallic cross-sectional area of a rope due to wear etc; they were not generally successful in detecting the presence of individual broken wires in a rope i.e. they looked at the average condition of the length of rope inside the instrument at any moment, rather than the very localised effects due to broken wires etc.

AC instruments were largely developed, and widely used, in South Africa and Canada where very deep mine shafts required hoisting systems in which the hoist ropes were so long that multilayer spooling on the hoist drums was the normal practice. Multilayer spooling causes zones of extra deterioration at the points where the rope at the end of one layer has to rise up the drum flange and turn before it can begin to form the next layer - so called "turn" damage. In addition the turns in the second layer lie in the grooves formed between the first layer turns but because of the opposite helical lay of the two layers on the drum each turn in the second layer has to jump out of one groove and cross-over into the next groove on every revolution of the drum - generating so called "cross-over" damage. Turn and cross-over damage are two of the characteristic types of deterioration found in multilayer drum hoisting systems which can be monitored successfully using AC instruments.

Today however AC instruments tend to have been largely superseded by the newer generation of instruments incorporating Hall-effect sensors, magnetometers, or special coils, which can monitor local defects as well as changes in the cross-sectional area.

3.2 DC and Permanent Magnet Instruments

DC and permanent magnet wire rope NDT instruments work on similar but not identical principles. The main difference is that the DC energised magnet tries to supply a constant magnetising force to the rope whilst a permanent magnet tries to supply a constant magnetic flux. In both types a length of rope is magnetised as it passes through the instrument. The magnetisation of the rope causes magnetic fringing fields to be set up round the length of rope between the pole pieces. These fringing fields are affected by discontinuities in the structure of the rope such as wear, corrosion, broken wires etc, and it is these which are monitored by the instrument. Ideally the magnets should be powerful enough to cause the length of rope between their pole pieces to reach magnetic saturation, but in some permanent magnet instruments ropes approaching the maximum physical size which can pass through them may not reach full saturation. This does not mean these ropes cannot be tested but if the instruments measure changes in the cross-sectional area of steel in the rope then these signals may be inaccurate, a point which should not be overlooked when the signals are analysed.

DC and permanent magnet instruments which use simple search coils are best suited for the detection of features which cause local discontinuities in the magnetic field generated round the rope e.g. broken wires, constructional distortions, corrosion, and localised damage. They are not, in their simplest form, suitable for monitoring uniform wear but the use of Hall effect sensors, flux-gate magnetometers, or special more advanced coil techniques in some of the newer instruments has overcome this disadvantage.

3.2.1 Search coil instruments

All the early DC and permanent magnet instruments which were commercially available in the UK utilised search coils to detect the changes in the fringing fields set up round the rope.

Some of the very early instruments used search coils which had to be wound individually round the rope before a test could be made. This avoided the problem of two half coils with many electrical connections between them, but this method was time consuming and not very practical. As the instruments developed, the simple search coil was soon replaced by two or more separate split coils which could be opened up like the magnet pole pieces to facilitate placing the instrument on the rope. These coils took many forms and were generally orientated in the instruments so that they monitored either the radial or the longitudinal components of the fringing fields.

One of the difficulties of using conventional search coils is that they measure the rate of change of the magnetic flux in the fringing field rather than the actual field strength, hence the coil output is sensitive to the speed of the rope through the magnet. To overcome this problem most of the instruments using detecting coils have speed compensation devices built into them using feedback voltages produced by some form of generator driven by movement of the rope through the instrument. These generators also provide signal pulses which can give an indication of the movement of the rope through the instrument.

There are also some instruments which contain multiple coils, and by comparing the signals generated in them it is possible to establish the approximate position of a defect within a rope.

Special types of amplification can be used to improve the signal-to-noise ratio, or more correctly the ratio between the amplitude of the defect signals and that of the background signals from the construction of the rope. These background signals are sometimes called the basic signature of the rope. This is an area where there have been substantial improvements over the last two decades and it is probably as much these which have contributed to

the advancement of the technique in recent years as changes in the
designs of the basic magnetic heads from which the data is collected.

In addition to the normal search coil type of instrument in which the
rate of change of the magnetic flux round the rope is monitored there
is also a new generation of instruments from the USA in which coils
are used to measure the flux flowing through the rope. These
instruments produce output signals, one of which is proportional to
the loss in metallic cross-sectional area (LMA) and can be calibrated
in these terms, and another which indicates qualitatively the
presence of local faults (LF) - they have the advantages of the
Hall-effect and magnetometer instruments mentioned below, and in some
respects may be argued to be an improvement over them, but so far
their performance has not equalled that of the best of the more
conventional search coil instruments with regard to the resolution of
closely spaced defects.

3.2.2 Hall-effect sensor and magnetometer instruments

Hall-effect sensors and magnetometers measure the actual strength of
the magnetic field in which they are placed rather than the rate of
change of the flux. They can therefore measure field strengths both
when the rope is moving through the magnet and theoretically at least
when it is stationary. Thus fringing fields caused by defects can be
located precisely by moving the rope very slowly through the
instrument. The signals from the sensors are not speed sensitive.

Hall-effect and magnetometer based instruments are good at detecting
local discontinuities due to broken wires, corrosion pitting etc but
those which are commercially available at the present time do not
have as good a resolution of closely spaced defects, especially in
locked-coil ropes, as the very best of the coil instruments (Fig.2).
Nevertheless for ropes of coarse construction e.g. 6x8(7/Δ)FC mine
haulage ropes, the ease of use of these instruments, especially when
defects have to be located exactly so that they can be also checked
visually, makes this type of instrument very useful.

These types of sensor can also be used to monitor changes in the
steel cross-sectional area (CSA) of the rope. This is accomplished by
placing the sensors either in the pole pieces so that they can
monitor the flux flowing into the rope to magnetise the rope up to
full saturation, or on a yoke round the rope in the centre of the
instrument to monitor the flux in the air space round the fully
saturated rope. When the CSA sensors are mounted in the centre of
each pole piece these, when added together, give an averaging effect
over the length of the rope inside the magnet at any moment. When the
CSA sensors are mounted on a yoke in the centre of the instrument,
close to the local defect sensors, they respond more immediately to
changes in steel area and consequently can indicate such changes over
much smaller distances. In some of the instruments the CSA and local

defect signals are combined into a single record but analysis is
generally much easier if the two signals are displayed separately.

3.2.3 Combined coil and Hall-effect or magnetometer instruments

Tests have shown that with the present generation of instruments
those with search coils, when correctly designed, give the best
resolution of small and closely spaced defects. Instruments which use
these together with additional sensors to monitor the cross-sectional
area of steel in a rope seem to give the best overall package for
many users. Such instruments would generally be best for monitoring
ropes of the more complex constructions such as locked-coil or
multistrand.

4. THE PRACTICAL APPLICATION OF NDT ON WIRE ROPES.

It should be emphasised that NDT tests do not generally replace
visual examinations except in a very few special cases. It is much
more usual for NDT to act as a aid to more efficient visual
examination. For example where long lengths of rope have to be
examined NDT can quickly assess the general condition of the rope and
identify the worst lengths where any following visual examination
should be concentrated. Thus the valuable time of the rope examiner
can be concentrated on inspecting the bad sections of the rope rather
than making overdetailed examination of the relatively good lengths.

There are of course other applications where environmental problems
or the construction of the rope prevent any really effective visual
inspections eg mast and chimney stays, underwater anchor cables and
tethers, and in installations using plastic coated ropes. In such
situations NDT examinations are often the only effective inspection
solution.

In general much more information can be obtained from NDT when the
tests are carried out periodically for this is the only really
satisfactory method of assessing gradually increasing levels of
deterioration such as those due to general wear or corrosion. It is
usual to carry out an initial NDT examination of a rope shortly after
its installation. Sufficient time should be allowed for the rope to
bed-in; this can vary from hours to days or even weeks depending on
the life expectancy of the rope. Once the rope has bedded-in then the
first NDT examination establishes a reference level from which later
deterioration can be estimated. It also reveals any anomalies from
manufacture, such as a broken wire or a missing length of wire from
one strand, which do sometimes occur. Periodic NDT examinations
should then be made at intervals determined by the overall life
expectancy of the rope. In many cases equal intervals would be chosen
initially but the frequency of examination might be increased towards
the end of the life of the rope with the growth of deterioration.

Periodic examinations give the rope operator the most useful data on
his ropes, and enable him to plan maintenance work or rope changes
more efficiently. However even single NDT examinations can give vital
information on such problems as internal deterioration, which often
cannot be gained from normal visual inspections whilst the rope
remains in service. Plastic coated ropes and ropes with thick
coatings of lubricant present no problems to this type of NDT
examination. These examinations, whether on a one-off basis or
carried out periodically, can quickly check the integrity of such
ropes, so that even a semi-skilled operator can easily identify any
problem area where there might be a substantial loss in the local
strength of the rope even if he cannot analyse the defect more
precisely.

5. PROBLEM AREAS

Accurate analysis of the signals from NDT instruments, whether
presented visually by means of flashing lights or on a chart
recorder, or audibly, is greatly aided if the operator has some
knowledge of the fundamental features of the magnetic method:

5.1 Magnetic saturation

With the DC energised or the permanent magnet method the depth of
penetration of the field into the rope is determined largely by the
strength of the magnet. If the magnet cannot saturate the rope,
defects near the centre of the rope may be missed.

At high rope speeds the eddy currents generated in the outer layers
as the rope passes through the magnet tend to hinder the further
penetration of the field within the finite time taken for a
particular length of rope to pass through the instrument, thus it is
usual to carry out the examinations at relatively low rope speeds. A
speed of around 1 m/s generally seems to give the optimum
performance. Rope speeds of up to about 3 m/s can be used in
situations where slower speeds are not available, and speeds of up to
5 m/s have been tried. At the higher speeds because of the restricted
penetration of the magnetic field in the rope the instruments
tend to respond only to surface defects or features such as changes
in the diameter of the rope.

Even without full magnetic saturation of the rope most instruments
can still give some valuable information to the rope examiner for
they should still detect any significant defect lying near the
surface of the rope. In practice, with probably the majority of
different rope constructions, the more serious defects are most
likely to occur either on the rope surface or close to it e.g. on the
underside of the outer strands.

Magnetic saturation becomes particularly important for those instruments which measure the cross-sectional area of steel in the rope as the signals from the area sensors are calibrated assuming full saturation.

5.2 Air gap and sensitivity

Many of the fringing fields generated round the smaller defects are themselves very small and difficult to detect especially if masked by overlying layers of wires. The closer the sensing elements are to the source of the anomaly in the fringing field the greater the chance of the defect being detected. Coils or sensors should therefore be positioned as close to the rope surface as practical for maximum resolution of small defects - the larger the air gap the weaker the fringing fields at the sensor position.

Many of the instruments are provided with a range of plug-in coils or sensors to fit different sizes of rope. Normally the clearance between the surface of the rope and the sensors should be of the order of a few millimetres only, sufficient to allow for small variations in the diameter of the rope to pass through the instrument without jamming. Some instruments utilise removable steel inserts inside their coils to reduce the air gap when testing small ropes. Several instruments are fitted with quick release or spring loaded catches to avoid the situation where distortion in the rope, say a displaced strand, can cause jamming of the rope as it passes through the instrument.

In tests it has been clearly shown that if a length of rope is known not to be distorted so that coils or sensors can be positioned very close to the surface of the rope the resolution of small defects is increased greatly. The resolution is of course also determined by factors such as the number and position of the sensors or the number of turns in the coils and their physical size and shape.

The ability of different instruments to resolve closely spaced defects into separate features depends very much on the type and design of the sensor/coil arrays. Instruments designed to detect defects in a coarse stranded rope such as a mine haulage rope may not be equally successful on a locked-coil hoisting rope. Figure 2 shows the response of two different instruments to an artificial defect in a locked-coil rope. This artificial defect consists of eighteen identical 4mm wide grooves spaced at 8mm centres in the second layer of the rope. The Hall-effect instrument, which had been specifically designed to examine stranded mine haulage ropes, simply produced a single large peak covering all eighteen grooves whereas a particular coil instrument designed by WBK's Seilprufstelle was able to indicate each of the eighteen grooves separately. Several other instruments were tested on this special locked-coil rope, all were able to detect the positions of the defects but very few were able to identify any of the separate grooves. All the instruments tested on this special rope are used widely and successfully for the NDT of stranded wire ropes but the tests illustrated that there were very large differences in their ability to resolve such closely spaced defects in a locked-coil rope.

5.3 Lateral oscillations of rope under pole pieces

In some instruments lateral oscillation of the rope as it passes through the magnet generates unwanted signals which can mask out defect signals. Oscillations arise mainly in situations where the instrument has to be towed along a stationary rope or where an instrument is held in one position on a moving rope by flexible ties. Wherever possible the instrument should be mounted onto something rigid. The use of small deflection pulleys on either side of the instrument, which may be part of the actual installation or mounted in a portable frame which can be inserted into the rope path at some suitable point, helps greatly in cutting down these movements. The effect of oscillations on the output signals from an instrument depends on the design of the coils or sensors arrays and how they are wired into the electrical circuit. In several of the newer instruments now commercially available these effects have been appreciably reduced.

5.4 Rope speed and rope speed variations

In many installations tests can be made with the rope passing through the instrument at a constant speed, either the normal operating speed of the installation or, where this is too high, at a slower speed usually provided by the equipment manufacturer for testing purposes. Generally rope speeds through the instruments from about 0.5 m/s to 2 m/s, or even 3 m/s with some types of rope, can be used, but the optimum speed seems to be around 1 m/s for most instruments. In this speed range most of the defect signal information from the rope is in the frequency range 0 - 120 Hz which can be recorded directly by some of the better chart recorders on the market. During the magnetisation of the rope as it passes through the instrument eddy currents are generated in the outer wires, especially when they lie in layers such as in locked-coil ropes. The fields generated by these eddy currents oppose and delay the further penetration of the magnetic flux into the rope. Consequently as it takes a finite time for the flux to build-up in the rope and this build-up has to be achieved within the time it takes a point in the rope to pass from the pole position to that of the sensors, there is effectively a maximum testing speed for any rope construction beyond which an NDT magnetic examination is impractical. If higher speeds are used then the instruments simply tend to respond only to variations in the external diameter of the rope or major surface defects.

Some of the more modern instruments are not speed sensitive but most of those using search coils are, and their manufacturer's usually

provide some form of speed compensation operated from a
tachogenerator running on the rope. Speed compensation by means of
feedback voltages is generally satisfactory around the normal testing
speeds but it oftens fails if very low creep speeds are used to try
to locate defects precisely. In practice the truly non speed
sensitive instruments have a big advantage in this area because
inevitably at some stage a rope examiner will want to locate a
defect precisely so that a more detailed visual inspection can be
made.

5.5 Instrument drift

In general the stability of the electronics used in modern
instruments is not a problem especially if the main aim of the
examination is the detection of localised defects such as broken
wires. The stability of the system becomes more of importance when
monitoring of the steel cross-sectional area is required on a long
rope e.g. cable belt ropes. It is also important where an instrument
has to be used in conditions different from those in which it has
been stored e.g. for monitoring haulage ropes underground. In these
conditions moving a large permanent magnet instrument from its point
of storage to the site of the examination, say from an underground
intake roadway to a much warmer return roadway, can involve an
appreciable thermal lag before all parts of the equipment stabilise
at the new temperature. Equilibrium may not be reached for several
hours and during this period the temperature differences between
different parts of the instrument, and between different parts of the
sensing head in particular, can prevent accurate calibration of the
sensors. The temperature stability of some of the Hall-effect sensors
10 to 15 years ago caused some difficulties but sensor manufacturers
now seem to have overcome this problem.

Temperature differences also cause problems due to condensation, an
important factor if a chart or tape recorder is needed at a
particular site.

5.6 Misleading or false signals

Misleading signals can be generated by errors in the alignment of the
magnet on the rope. As mentioned earlier the distance between a
defect and the sensing element should be as small as possible for
maximum detection sensitivity and the highest resolution between
closely spaced defects. For the optimum all round sensitivity the
rope should pass through the instrument centred on the main axis of
the coil or sensor array. If the rope lies off the centre-line then
defects on the side of the rope closest to the sensors will generate
larger signals than those on the opposite side, so the defects on one
side of the rope may be detected whilst similar defects on the
opposite side are not.

In some instruments physical contact between the rope and the pole pieces of the magnet can generate false signals. In practice this seems to be mainly of concern in the smaller hand held instruments if it is possible to move them relative to the axis of the rope whilst pushing the magnet head along the rope. Randomly produced signals such as these could be extremely confusing to new operators but, if suspected, can be distinguished from genuine defect signals by passing the instrument over the same length of rope several times when only the latter should appear consistently at the same point.

Some instruments, primarily those with chart or tape recorder outputs, can be affected by mains interference especially if testing is being carried out on a site where there are large electrical generators or motors, or where high current switching occurs e.g. near arc furnaces.

5.7 Limitations

The fundamental requirement for this type of NDT is that the rope must be made of a magnetic material. This rules out the testing of most stainless steel ropes and cables made of aluminium or copper etc, though these instruments can be used to detect defects in the steel armouring around some aluminium or copper cables.

For any defect to be detectable it must of course induce a discontinuity into the fringing field round the rope. General experience has shown that with most instruments the broken ends of a wire must move apart by 1mm or more before the defect is certain to be detected. With six or eight strand ropes, where the main load is carried by the outer wires in each strand, the ends of broken strand outer wires usually have little difficulty in moving sideways into the gaps between the strands. With this lateral displacement of the wire ends the discontinuity in the fringing field is large and detection of the breaks is relatively easy. In a locked-coil rope on the other hand the wires in the inner layers are all held tightly in place by the adjacent wires in the same layer and in the layers above and below. The broken ends of a wire have therefore to move axially along the rope before a gap large enough to be detected is formed. Generally therefore the signals from a defect in a locked-coil rope are very much smaller than those from a stranded rope and consequently much more difficult to detect.

A third very important limitation of this technique is that the instruments cannot examine the length of rope immediately adjacent to the rope termination - and this is probably the most vulnerable area in most rope systems due to the effects of both lateral oscillations of the rope and variations in its axial loading. For mine hoisting ropes in the UK this problem length has traditionally been dealt with by cutting off the rope termination and recapping the rope at intervals of six months. However with the more modern friction winder installations, which cause less damage to the rope in this region, much longer intervals between recappings are now being investigated. Ropes of fixed lengths, such as bridge hangers, cannot be dealt with in the same manner and it is possible that other NDT methods e.g. ultrasonics, would be of greater value in this critical area, with the magnetic method supplying general information about the main length of the hangers away from the terminations.

6. DEFECT SIGNAL ANALYSIS

The output from the different types of instrument can be presented either audibly or visually. An audible indication that a defect has passed through the instrument immediately alerts the rope examiner that the rope could contain defects which require further investigation, but they do little to tell him anything about the type of defect. At best he may note that the defect seems to be a single isolated defect or that a certain length of rope contains many defects. He should also be able to distinguish between defects spaced at intervals along a length and those closely bunched at one point, though with some instruments multiple defects at one point would produce a single audible bleep which would be undistinguishable from that from a single defect.

There are also several instruments which could be described as having audible/visual outputs e.g. in addition to a simple audible bleep the instrument shows one or more flashing lights, usually LEDs, when the sensors detect a defect. Where more than one LED is used the number which light up at each defect is usually directly related to the amplitude of the analogue signal from the sensors. In practice watching an LED display for long periods of time can be extremely tiring so some instruments have LEDs which are triggered, if the analogue signal exceeds certain preset levels, and then remain on until reset.

Both of the above types of instrument can be regarded as essentially inspection tools i.e. they draw the attention of the rope examiner to damaged or deteriorated lengths of the ropes which should then be subjected to more detailed visual inspection. They cannot generally be used for diagnostic purposes unless the instrument also produces a chart or tape recorder output. Once the analogue output is recorded in some way then much more information can be gained from an NDT examination.

From chart recordings of the analogue signals it is readily apparent where additional deterioration has taken place since the previous NDT examination by simply laying the traces side by side with some easily identifiable feature on the two traces close together. Such a check on the overall condition of the rope may take only a few minutes but can give essential information on when a rope should be changed.

A chart recording can give much more data on the state of the rope in general, and in particular it can highlight zones of more advanced deterioration in otherwise good ropes so that the causes of the deterioration can be sought and the appropriate remedial action taken.

If individual defects warrant much deeper investigation then a chart recording becomes an essential feature. The first chart record should be a single trace covering the whole of the rope for this indicates the general state of the rope and whether any defects occur in localised groups or whether they are fairly equally distributed along the whole length of the rope. At this stage it is usually possible to distinguish between single defects and multiple defects at any point. Figure 3 illustrates the difference between the records from a Hall-effect sensor instrument of a single wire break and multiple breaks at the same spot. The trace on the left is on a scale which might be used for the initial examination, the trace on the right was made with an expanded record, i.e. higher chart speed.

The first general chart record also identifies the position of the defects relative to features such as rope splices. Figure 4 shows short sections of two traces from a mine haulage rope, one obtained using a coil instrument, and the other from a Hall-effect instrument. The traces show the response of the two instruments to a long splice and to patches of corrosion.

On the spot visual examination of the rope at the positions of the indicated faults can usually quickly confirm the presence and nature of the defects. The signals recorded from any single defect do have certain characteristic forms depending on whether the sensing units respond to the radial or longitudinal component of the fringing field. The characteristic forms of say broken wires, depend on the gap between the two ends of the break (Fig.5). Thus by studying enlarged traces of the magnetic field anomalies caused by the defects it is possible for a lot of additional information to be obtained from them. Figure 6 illustrates some of the measurements which might be needed before a detailed analysis of an individual defect could be made. One way of producing the enlarged traces would be to pass the instrument repeatedly over an indicated defect with the chart speed, and possibly the amplifier gain, increased. However such action, if there are many defects to be investigated, would be extremely time consuming and hardly practical. If the signals are recorded on a tape recorder as well as on a chart recorder then the more detailed traces can be produced at a later, probably more convenient time, and the records are available in a suitable form for further analysis at any time.

Various authors have demonstrated the effects on both the radial and longitudinal components of the fringing field of different gaps between the ends of a single broken wire (Fig.5). When more than one break occurs at the same point the effects on the fringing field become much more complex with almost infinite variations possible. For a single defect it is possible to use these characteristics to work back from the actual defect record to estimate its effect on the strength of a rope. Such analysis has been carried out in Poland and papers published in that country over many years have presented various graphs and calibration curves to help in such work. Certainly for single defects an estimate can be made of the effects of simple breaks on the strength of the rope but the process is very time consuming. Estimates carried out in this manner in the UK have suggested that the technique is more suited to a research laboratory rather than for use on site. When the records suggest multiple defects at the same point, a much more serious case for the rope examiner, this type of analysis would, in the author's opinion, be extremely difficult to carry out in practice.

Multiple breaks at the same spot in one layer have different effects on the output trace if the gaps between the ends of the broken wires do, or do not, overlap each other. Multiple breaks which occur in different layers can display very different effects from breaks in the same layer. Thus any detailed analysis of such breaks would probably only be attempted in very special circumstances where the time and effort needed for the analysis were clearly justified.

If many breaks occur in the same wire, say due to a drawing defect during manufacture, then the instruments cannot identify this fact, and on the charts the breaks appear the same as if they had been distributed in several different wires. Only a careful visual examination would reveal this feature.

The addition of sensors to monitor cross-sectional area of steel in a rope is advantageous in some situations - especially those where external wear is a prominent feature. Such sensors also usually give a very characteristic signal when passing over a corroded length of rope (Fig.4). These signals would alert a rope examiner to the presence of internal or external corrosion but it is not easy to interpret the results in a quantitative manner. It should be noted that with stranded ropes uniform normal external wear affects all the outer wires in each strand in the outer layer of strands, not just those which happen to lie on the strand crowns at any one position. Consequently the loss in strength is much greater than that suggested by looking at the cross-section of the rope at one position.

When any magnetic NDT examination is carried out on an undamaged rope signals are produced by the sensor system which have certain characteristic frequencies. These small output signals are repeatable and may be regarded as the background signature of that particular rope. Frequency domain analysis has shown that the signals are made up of many frequencies but that there is a correlation between the frequencies and the lay lengths of the wires in the different layers of the rope or strand.

It would be very useful, and at first it seems quite feasible, to use computer techniques to extract the deterioration signals from those of the background rope signature. Unfortunately this is not a simple task of subraction because most ropes undergo slight changes in their construction during their service life. For example there is an initial stretch when a rope is first loaded and then subsequently more gradual creep occurs. In many ropes the modulus of the rope probably also changes during its service life. In applications where ropes hang vertically there is a self weight elastic stretch component but at any point this can alter during service if recapping samples are cut off the rope and new rope let off the spare turns of the drum to compensate.

7. RECENT DEVELOPMENTS

7.1 Hand held instruments for small ropes

The recent appearance of several small hand-held instruments for small ropes up to about 22mm dia has introduced NDT to a new range of customers. These instruments have audible/visual outputs and can be used without a chart recorder simply to verify whether or not a rope contains broken wires. They may be regarded as inspection tools rather than diagnostic instruments though many may be converted to the latter by simply plugging-in a recorder.

7.2 IS instruments for underground use in mines

For safe use underground in coalmines electrical equipment has to meet certain standards of flameproofness (FLP) or it has to be made intrinsically safe (IS) so that in a mine atmosphere which could contain methane there is no danger of its use causing an explosion. There are also other restrictions on the materials from which the equipment can be manufactured e.g. in general the use of any aluminium component is banned because of the danger of incendive sparking if an aluminium component strikes rusty steel. After many years of trying to persuade instrument manufacturers to produce an instrument to meet UK IS requirements at a reasonable cost British Coal have developed their own instrument primarily for the examination of underground manriding haulage ropes and are now working on one for use on locked-coil ropes. Details are given in the following paper by A K Coultate.

8. THE FUTURE

8.1 Instruments for special applications

Although permanent magnet instruments seem the best for general purpose use there are one or two special cases where instruments based on DC energised magnets might be beneficial.

Large cable belt installations such as that at the Selby Mine Complex use very long expensive ropes. These could perhaps be best monitored by permanent installations of NDT instruments on both ropes. The use of DC energised magnets would avoid the situation where the magnets would need frequent cleaning to remove any steel debris or broken off wire ends picked up from the rope. Such magnets could be switched on, and left running for just sufficient time for the whole length of the rope to pass through the instrument, once a day or once a week as required. Counting the number of signal peaks above a certain size on each occasion would immediately alert the rope examiner to any increase in the numbers of broken wires, and give an indication of the rate of deterioration. Such switching on and off of the instrument and the counting of the signal peaks could be easily automated. Fault density counters could be included which could operate a warning signal and a rope marking device if the density of the faults exceeded a pre-set value at any point.

Where a very large rope or spiral strand, such as an offshore tether, needs testing the practicalities of using permanent magnets raises problems because of their physical size and weight. In such situations DC energised magnets seem worth considering.

8.2 Signal processing

The most important feature of any wire rope NDT equipment is its ability to detect broken wires and other defects wherever they occur in the structure of the rope. Once the defect has been detected the instrument designer can choose a number of alternatives ways of displaying the information to aid the rope examiner. The signal can be amplified in various ways to produce different signal to background signature and noise levels. These can then be fed to tape recorders, chart recorders, or simply displayed digitally so that only a count of the signal peaks is presented. In addition the signal peaks can easily be made to operate a rope defect marking device such as an aerosol paint spray. If a rope movement derived signal from a pulse generator operated through a wheel running on the rope is also available, then signal delay line techniques can be used to control the operation of the marking device. These can delay the operation of a paint spray until the defect has reached its position, perhaps one metre downstream from the detecting head of the instrument. Such devices use only simple electronics and with them it has been shown possible to accurately mark the position of a defect in the rope to within 2cm at normal NDT rope testing speeds.

Using the same pulse generator to monitor the length of rope which has passed through the instrument it is possible to design fault density counters which are of more importance to the rope examiner than simple fault (signal peak) counters. For example, in a long rope

there could be many hundreds of broken wires scattered along its
length without any substantial loss in strength. Alternatively there
could be a few dozen breaks in a short length with serious loss in
strength over that short length only. By using counters which reset
after a pre-selected movement of the rope, e.g. at 1/2m or 1m
intervals, signal processors can produce a rough density measurement.
The problem with any fault density measuring device is that if a
short patch of closely spaced faults passes through the instrument it
is essential that the whole patch of breaks (or signal peaks) should
be counted together - not split into two groups by the counter
resetting itself in the middle of the patch. If several overlapping
resettable counters are included it is possible to get reasonable
response to short groups of defects. For example four counters all
counting signal peaks over a 1m distance but offset relative to each
other so that they are reset in turn every 1/4m have been shown to
give a good coverage of most patches of defects. A prototype fault
density monitor of this type was developed by the HSE in Sheffield
some years ago. If the density of the breaks exceeds a selected
preset value then it is easy get the signal processor to mark the
affected length on the rope, operate some form of alarm system, and
in the worst case to initiate the automatic shut down of the
installation. Similarly signal processing can usually separate the
peaks due to outer wire breaks from those generated by broken inner
layer wires or filler wires, and these can then be sent to different
counters if required.

9. LEGAL ASPECTS

Section 26 of the Factories' Act 1961 requires that wire ropes are
subjected to thorough examination by a competent person at intervals
not exceeding six months. Other legislation has similar requirements.
How the examination is to be carried out is not specified. However in
other parts of the legislation, references are made to patent defects
and visible broken wires. This merely lists two aspects of the
thorough examination and does not imply that these are the only
aspects. Bearing in mind the date of the legislation, these
references reflect the rope and examination technology of the time
and the inference should not be drawn that the visual aspect is the
only component of a thorough examination.

Now that better ways of performing the examination are available, and
having regard to the increasingly complex construction of the ropes
themselves, it is the author's opinion that modern ropes require
modern examination technology and that, in many cases, NDT methods
constitute the only practical way of performing a thorough
examination.

10. CONCLUSIONS

The non-destructive examination of wire ropes has advanced a long way in the last 20 years. There are now magnetic instruments commercially available which can monitor all but perhaps the largest offshore cables. Improvements in sensor technology and signal processing are making the interpretation of the instrument records easier. The effectiveness of traditional visual inspection and examination techniques is severely restricted on some of the rope constructions now in use, and where deterioration occurs internally; the magnetic NDT method has been shown to be a more efficient method of rope examination in these cases, and in most other situations especially where long ropes are involved or where ropes are used in dark or dirty environments. The author expects to see the use of NDT instruments increase greatly over the next decade as their advantages become more appreciated.

REFERENCES

(1) Chaplin R C and Potts A E "Wire Rope in Offshore Applications", The Marine Technology Directorate Ltd, London, 1988.

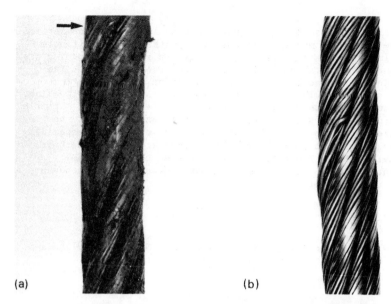

Fig 1. A defect (a) almost invisible during service under a coating of lubricant and dirt, and (b) after cleaning the rope.

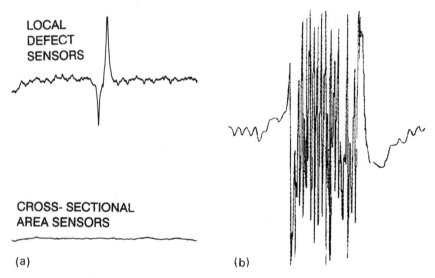

Fig 2. A large 18 groove artificial defect in a test rope as indicated by (a) a Hall-effect instrument and (b) a coil instrument.

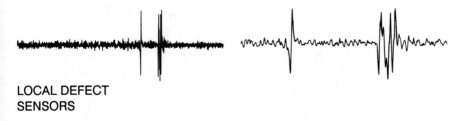

LOCAL DEFECT
SENSORS

EXPANDED RECORD

CROSS- SECTIONAL
AREA SENSORS

Fig 3. Traces from single and multiple broken wires

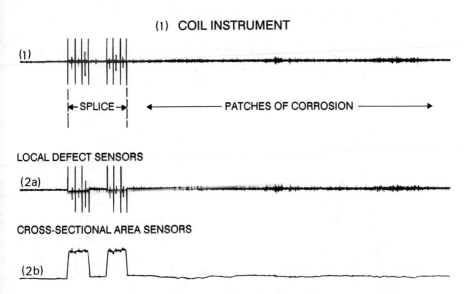

(1) COIL INSTRUMENT

(1)

|← SPLICE →| ◄─────────── PATCHES OF CORROSION ───────────►

LOCAL DEFECT SENSORS

(2a)

CROSS-SECTIONAL AREA SENSORS

(2b)

(2) HALL- EFFECT SENSOR INSTRUMENT

**Fig 4. Traces from a mine haulage rope showing a long splice and
a length of corroded rope.**

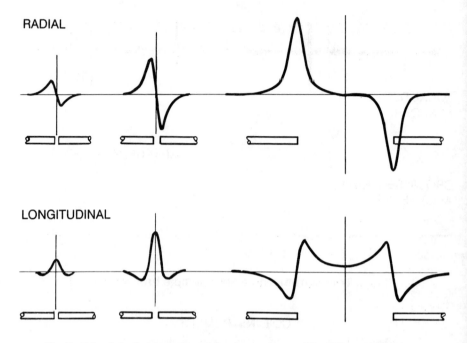

Fig 5. Fringing fields around broken wires with different distances between the broken ends

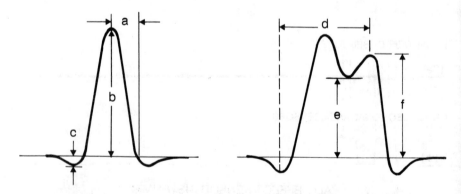

Fig 6. Examples of some of the measurements needed for detailed analysis of the longitudinal fringing fields associated with short and long defects.

NON-DESTRUCTIVE TESTING OF WIRE ROPE WITHIN BRITISH COAL

by

A K COULTATE*

SUMMARY

This paper describes the three main applications for wire rope within British Coal.

Inspection practices are currently based on visual examination procedures. The advantages of NDT are described, along with development of intrinsically safe NDT equipment for use in the examination of underground haulage and shaft guide ropes. Problems with the examination of locked coil winding ropes are also discussed and the work currently being undertaken to develop a viable NDT system for these ropes is described.

1. INTRODUCTION

British Coal (BC) operate ninety six deep coal mines in the United Kingdom. Each of these mines uses at least two entries for access underground, which can either consist of vertical shafts or inclined drifts. The entries are necessary for the transport of men to and from the coal faces, materials to the coal faces, coal out of the mine and ventilation purposes. The mining operations make extensive use of wire ropes, which fall into three broad categories:-

Stranded ropes   - haulage of men and materials
half locked coil ropes   - shaft guides
full locked coil ropes   - winding or hoisting

*A K Coultate, BSc C.Eng, MIM works in the Field Metallurgy Group, Metallurgy and Materials Branch, British Coal, Headquarters Technical Department.

All of the above ropes deteriorate in service and are therefore subject to examination procedures and removal criteria, for which appropriate practices have evolved over many years experience. These practices have resulted in a system of safe wire rope usage based on visual rope examinations and removal from service of ropes on the basis of condition and time of service, depending on the application. There are two possible disadvantages of this system, firstly, deterioration might not be detected by visual means alone which adversely affects the safe usage of the rope, and secondly many ropes may be removed from service when they have not actually suffered any significant deterioration, which adversely affects the economic usage of the ropes.

The application of NDT can vastly improve the inspection procedures such that deterioration that would otherwise not have been found by visual inspection can readily be detected. Also, because rope condition can be more reliably assessed, rope can be used to its full potential.

2.   CURRENT EXAMINATION PRACTICE

Ropes used within BC for carrying personnel are subjected to two types of routine visual examination (Ref 1). Regulations state that:-

i.   All ropes should be inspected once at least in every 24 hours

ii. All ropes shall be given a thorough examination not less than once in every month. In this instance ropes are thoroughly cleaned at points liable to deterioration and examined externally for wear, corrosion, broken wires and other damage.

Such work is carried out by a variety of experienced and competent personnel dependent on, for instance, application, site position and local practice, and would be ropemen, blacksmiths or fitters.

Removal of ropes from service is governed by two main criteria, namely condition and life, and these are best quoted directly from the Ropeman's Handbook (Ref 1):-

"As a general rule no rope should remain in service:-

i)   When the engineer considers that the factor of safety has become too low (when the reserve of strength is no longer sufficient to ensure that the rope can safely withstand the repeated shock loads, bends etc).

ii)   When the loss in rope strength due to wear, corrosion, or both is approaching one-sixth or 16 per cent of the original strength (or any lesser value set by the Engineer).

iii) When the loss in rope strength due to fatigue, corrosion-fatigue, or surface embrittlement, or due to cracked or broken wires of any kind, is approaching one-tenth or 10 per cent of the original strength (or any lesser value set by the Engineer). The loss in strength may be estimated by regarding all broken or cracked wires within a length of two rope lays as no longer contributing any strength to that part of the rope.

iv)   When the outer wires have lost about one-third or 33 per cent of their depth as a result of any form of deterioration.

v)   When the outer wires are becoming loose and displaced for any reason.

vi)   When the rope has become kinked or otherwise deformed, distorted, or damaged, and the affected part cannot be cut out.

vii) When the rope has been subjected to a severe overwind or overload, or to severe shock loading, as a result of an accident.

viii) When examination of the rope leaves any doubt as to its safety, on any grounds.

ix)   When a rope, which is still in good condition, reaches the maximum statutory life for its type, as laid down in Regulations or the maximum life specified by the Engineer."

Pre-determined lives on ropes are set, dependent on the specific application.

Lives specified for manriding haulage ropes are dependent on local Area policy and application and can be for instance 12 months or 24 months, up to a maximum 30 months.

In the case of shaft guide ropes, a maximum life of 20 years is recommended.

The maximum life of a winding rope is 3½ years as defined by the Mines and Quarries Act, although this can be extended in exceptional circumstances with permission from the Health and Safety Executive. The 3½ year life is applicable to drum winder ropes only, In the case of friction winder ropes, British Coal's own regulations limit the life to 2 years.

3.   NDT - HAULAGE ROPES USED FOR MANRIDING

   3.1   The Ropes

   There are several thousand rope haulage installations in use within BC. The majority are used for the transport of materials, but an estimated 200 are used for manriding. A plan of a typical endless manriding haulage installation is shown in Fig 1. Typically, such installations are used on surface drifts or underground, and gradients vary from level to steeper than 30%. The haulage length can vary from several hundred to in excess of three thousand metres. The haulage ropes are typically of triangular strand construction, although some round strand ropes are used, and they range from 19 to 38 mm diameter. The range of ropes used is a rationalised selection from BS302 Part 5. (Ref 2).

   Deterioration of the rope is dependent on the specific condition of the installation viz geometry, mechanical condition and environment. The principal deterioration is:-

   i)   Wear - external - abrasive - rope rubs along the floor or
                                            against other objects.
                        - plastic - high bearing pressures
              - internal - nicking - high pressures
                        - abrasive - poor lubrication

   ii)   Corrosion - external - environment, poor lubrication
                   - internal - environment, poor lubrication

   iii) Broken wires - fatigue - bending
                               - plastic wear
                               - martensitic embrittlement

   iv)   Kinks and other damage

   Two factors demanded that improved inspection procedures be developed for manriding haulage ropes. These were:-

   i)   A tendency towards the use of higher haulage speeds (some in excess of 20 kmph) called for improved rope integrity.

ii) When rope failures have occurred, many have resulted from internal corrosion and/or wear which has not been detected by visual inspection

3.2 NDT Equipment

It was decided that visual inspection of haulage ropes should be improved by the use of some form of NDT equipment which should fulfill certain criteria. The equipment must:-

- be capable of detecting all of the types of deterioration encountered.

- be electrically intrinsically safe (IS) for use in underground coal mine atmospheres.

- must produce consistent results so that rope deterioration with time can be monitored.

- be portable and capable of being used in a mining environment, ie pitworthy.

- be relatively simple to use so that it can be operated by a wide range of personnel; eg by the ropeman as an aid to his visual examinations to guide him to the worst sections of rope, or by an NDT operator as a diagnostic tool.

Investigations revealed that the electromagnetic NDT technique offered a practical method of examining the ropes. Alternating current (AC) instruments did not meet any of the requirements, while the permanent magnet or DC types appeared more promising. The new breed of equipment which can detect local faults and metallic cross section has ably met the requirements for detection of deterioration in the ropes Comparative trials with a wide variety of commercially available equipment have been carried out, and this coupled with extensive use in the field, has demonstrated the practical advantages to be gained. However, none of the commercially available equipment fully met BC's requirements, the principal limitation being that they were not IS. After several attempts to acquire IS equipment, BC have developed their own IS certified NDT system.

The NDT system developed at BC's Headquarters Technical Department consists of a permanent magnet test head and an electronic control box (Fig 2).

The test head weighs approximately 29 kg. Two hinges join the top and bottom assemblies together such that, when opened, they can be slipped apart so that the two halves of the test head may be separated; this allows for easy transport and positioning around the rope. Rope guide tubes are fitted into the bore of the test head in order to retain the rope in a near-central position and prevent excessive lateral movement during an examination. Different rope guides are fitted dependent on the size of rope to be examined, and they are treated as consumable items in that they will eventually wear out with use.

A sensor unit, fitted around the mid-point of the test head, is used to detect deterioration in the rope under test. Two parameters are detected by this sensor unit, namely local faults (broken wires and other damage) and metallic cross sectional area (wear and corrosion). The length of rope that passes through the test head is measured by a transducer assembly fitted to a spring wheel which is positioned at one end of the test head.

The test head is connected to an electronic control box via leads and large Plessey-type multipin plugs and sockets which are both robust and reliable.

The electronic control box (Fig 2) weighs approximately 8 kg and is carried by a leather shoulder strap. The control box performs two major functions. Firstly, outputs from the test head are processed and displayed via LEDs and LCDs so that basic information regarding the presence of broken wires, corrosion, splices and distance along the rope is presented. This allows the equipment to be used as an aid to the ropeman's visual examination, to guide him to deteriorating sections of rope. Secondly, outputs are provided in a form suitable for recording onto IS and non-IS recording equipment.

3.3 Site Tests

Over 300 examinations of haulage ropes have been carried out up to December 1988 using NDT equipment. Initially, the majority of the examinations were carried out using prototype rope test equipment manufactured by Plessey.

During this period the ability of NDT to detect and identify deterioration was established. The ability to monitor deterioration was similarly established, and the advantages of using NDT became apparent. Not only can safety be improved, but the greater information that becomes available to the rope operator allows for optimum performance to be obtained from the rope.

The BC rope test instrument was first used on-site in late summer 1987, when it was used alongside the Plessey equipment. After comparative trials both on-site and on test installations, the BC equipment has been used extensively; to December 1988, 67 examinations have been successfully carried out. In terms of sensitivity, consistency and stability of results, the IS equipment has met the requirements expected of it.

To date, results from the equipment have always been recorded and this is done in one of two ways. At surface installations, the outputs are recorded on tape and displayed simultaneously onto chart paper so that an immediate assessment of rope condition can be made (Figs 3 & 4). At underground installations, the outputs are recorder on magnetic tape, and are then fed into a chart recorder on the surface (Fig 5). Simultaneously, the display on the electronic control box is observed so that incidences of deterioration can be seen and, where necessary, the rope can be examined visually.

Various examples of results are shown in Figs 6 to 9. Fig 6 is taken from a rope which contains broken wires; the two sets of results taken several weeks apart also demonstrate the consistency of the results. Fig 7 demonstrates a severe case of internal corrosion. Fig 8 shows how a region of heavy local deterioration can be identified and repaired. Where wires break through fatigue, a characteristic deterioration curve may be constructed (Fig 9) which, although not an indication of the worst rope section, gives useful information regarding the overall condition and can be used to compare the performance of subsequent ropes.

The haulage rope test instrument which has been developed at BC's Headquarters Technical Department is to be manufactured under licence by Hawker Siddeley Dynamic Engineering, and there are currently several instruments on order for use throughout the BC coalfields.

4. SHAFT GUIDE ROPES

The majority of BC shafts use ropes to both guide the conveyance and also to keep the two conveyances separated so that collision with each other and with the shaft sides does not occur. The ropes used are half-locked coil construction, and range from 29 mm to 51 mm diameter. They are typically suspended by either wedge clamps or cast conical cones and held in tension at the bottom either by cheese weights or a spring tensioning device.

Deterioration of the ropes is dependent on mechanical and
environmental conditions. The main mechanism of deterioration is
wear caused by the conveyance guides which rub against the rope.
This rubbing is influenced by lateral movement of the cage caused
by draughts adjacent to ventilation fans and insets, and at
positions where the conveyance stops and starts on a periodic
basis. Added to this is the environment, which can be anything

from dry through to very wet; the water may be highly corrosive;
temperature can vary between very cold and hot. Corrosion can
therefore play a significant part in the deterioration of the
ropes.

Guide ropes can be examined using NDT equipment, presently either
the BC haulage rope system up to 41 mm diameter, or other,
commercially available equipment for the full range of rope sizes.
The test head is typically clamped around the guide rope
immediately above the conveyance, and secured to the conveyance.
Electrical recording equipment can be positioned on top of or
inside the conveyance. A descent of the shaft is made, and the
length of rope from the surface to pit bottom examined. If
required, the test head can be slung under the conveyance so that
rope in the sump can also be examined.

A typical set of results is shown in Fig 10. Not only does NDT
indicate the condition along the continuous length of the rope,
which is a big advantage over visual inspection practices, it has
also been found that the NDT results accurately reflect losses in
mechanical strength in the ropes.

5. WINDING ROPES

The majority of mines employ two shafts, each shaft employing in
the main 2-rope drum winders, although some mines use multi-rope
friction winders. Over 95% of the winding ropes are of full locked
coil construction, in the size range 16-57 mm diameter. Dependent
on the specific installation, they can deteriorate in several ways.
Externally, the rope may suffer wear of the outer wires, surface
corrosion, or failure through fatigue. Distortion of the rope is
also a problem which can occur. All of these features can be
examined and identified visually. Internally, wires can wear,
corrode (which is mainly a problem in friction winder ropes which
are lubricated only sparingly), break through fatigue, distort and
cause other damage, none of which can be detected by visual
examination while the rope is in service. The very dense steel
structure of the ropes coupled to the mechanism of failure within
the ropes makes them notoriously difficult to reliably examine
using NDT methods. For instance, there is often

poor separation between broken wire ends, which produces very little magnetic disturbance to be detected, and this is further "masked" by one or more layers of wires covering the fracture. It follows that an NDT instrument must be extremely sensitive to small magnetic disturbances caused by these internal faults.

Experience has shown that instruments of "average" sensitivity eg the BC haulage rope instrument, and the majority of other commercially available equipments, are unsuitable for the examination of locked coil ropes. This has also been found elsewhere (Ref 3).

Following from experience gained in building the haulage rope test equipment, a second set of equipment suitable for the examination of locked coil winding ropes is under development. It differs from the earlier equipment in that it is built to examine ropes up to 64 mm diameter, and is also non-IS. More importantly, its sensing system is being refined to give optimum sensitivity and resolution between defects. Figure 11 shows it undergoing a site test.

Two further areas of work are being carried out. Firstly, ropes are being monitored in service in order to determine changes occurring through their lives. Secondly, ropes are being opened up and examined in order to correlate what has been indicated by the NDT equipment with what is actually present in the rope.

Ultimately, a reliable monitoring system for locked coil winding ropes will have been developed.

6. CONCLUSIONS

Extensive monitoring and post-service examinations have shown that haulage and guide ropes are ideally suited to NDT. Their costruction and mechanisms of failure mean that deterioration can be both detected and identified with a high degree of reliability.

Significant advantages over visual examination procedures are therefore gained in the aspect of safety and also in the optimisation of rope usage.

Problems exist in the detection of deterioration inside locked coil winding ropes, and work is being carried out with a view to maximising the benefits to be gained by NDT. Results to date are encouraging.

It is important to understand the characteristics of the rope under examination, and also the capabilities of the NDT equipment in order that NDT can be carried out reliably and safely. This is especially important with locked coil ropes, and probably in other complex rope constructions also, where it is likely that all deterioration may not be detected by NDT. It then becomes very important to know what is not, as well as what is being detected by the NDT equipment. However, provided that the NDT procedures are understood, then there are many advantages to be gained from this type of testing.

Acknowledgement

The author would like to thank Mr C T Massey, Head of Technical Department, for permission to publish this paper. Opinions expressed in the paper are those of the author and not necessarily those of British Coal.

7.   REFERENCES

1.   Ropeman's Handbook, published by the National Coal Board (now British Coal Corporation).

2.   BS 302:Part 5:1987 Stranded steel wire ropes - Specification for ropes for hauling purposes.

3.   Non-Destructive Testing of Wire Ropes: Tests on the Performance of seven instruments mainly on locked coil wire hoisting ropes, by the Health and Safety Executive with aid from the Commision of European Communities, Edited by Dr C H H Corden, RLSD, Sheffield, 1980.

TYPICAL HAULAGE INSTALLATION

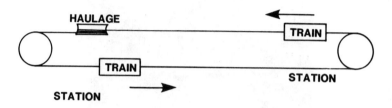

Figure 1   Plan of a typical endless haulage system used for manriding

Figure 2   General view of the intrinsically safe rope test system (approximately 1/8 scale size).

41

Figure 3   View of the IS rope test equipment being used to inspect a 26 mm diameter haulage rope.

Figure 4   Close up of the IS test head on a 26 mm diameter haulage rope.

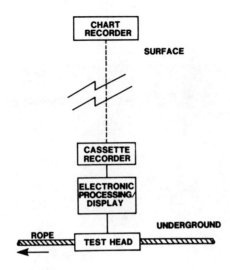

Figure 5   Scheme for using the IS equipment underground

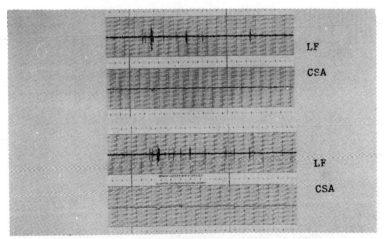

Figure 6   Results from a haulage rope containing broken wires.
The upper trace was taken several weeks before the lower
trace. The results demonstrate the ability to monitor
deterioration along the rope, and also the
reproducibility of the equipment outputs.
LF = local faults
CSA = cross sectional area

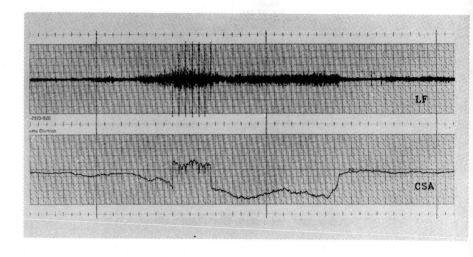

Figure 7   Severe internal corrosion.

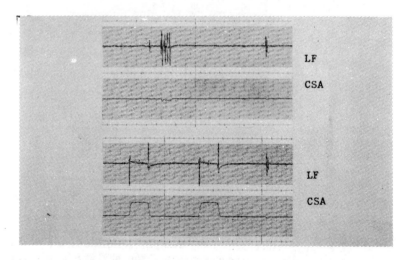

Figure 8   Severe local deterioration in one strand of a haulage
rope has been identified in the top trace. The damage
was subsequently eliminated by a strand repair, shown in
the lower trace.

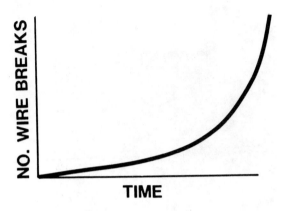

Figure 9   Total number of broken wires detected in a rope versus
time gives a characteristic deterioration curve for an
installation.

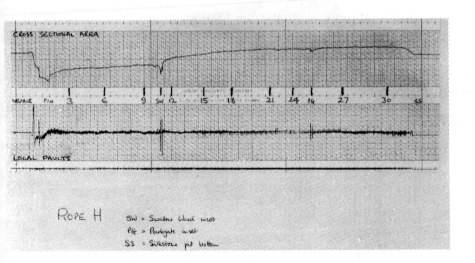

Figure 10   Results taken from a 41 mm diameter half locked coil
guide rope.

Figure 11   Prototype test head installed around a 45 mm diameter
locked coil winding rope.

WIRE ROPE NON-DESTRUCTIVE TESTING IN POLAND - EQUIPMENT, METHODS OF TESTING AND STATUTORY REGULATIONS

J. HANSEL, L. LANKOSZ AND W. OLEKSY

Since 1974 obligatory periodic magnetic rope testings for Polish passenger ropeways have been carried on and at the end of the seventies the Polish mining regulations included the obligatory periodic magnetic testing of winding ropes. This paper describes the magnetic instruments manufactured in Poland and development trends of rope NDT equipment. The paper also discusses statutory regulations, standards and organisation of wire rope magnetic testings in Poland. The economic and operational effects of rope non-destructive testings are also presented.

GENERAL INFORMATION CONCERNING POLISH EQUIPMENT AND METHODS APPLIED FOR MAGNETIC TESTING OF WIRE ROPES

The pressure for better use of constructional material and the tendency towards increasing reliability and safety has been the driving force of progress in the field of instrumental, non-destructive measuring methods used for assessing the condition of wire ropes.

Among the quick, non-destructive methods suitable for testing wire ropes magnetic testing, known as magnetic defectoscopy, is presently recognized as the most objective way to assess wire ropes.

The rudiments of magnetic defectoscopy of wire ropes in Poland date back to the 1940's. The University of Mining and Metallurgy in Kraków started working on this subject in 1946 (Kawecki and Stachurski (1), Kawecki and Hansel (2)). The work has looked into topics of a complex character including theoretical and experimental studies on the relationship between the defectograph signal traces and the actual weakening of the rope, on improving the instruments and the implementation of magnetic testing in the industry.

Stanislaw Staszic University of Mining and Metallurgy,
 Interbranch Laboratory for Wire Rope Testing and Rope Transport Equipment.
 Al. Mickiewicza 30, 30-059 Kraków, Poland

Knowledge of the technique and the availability of the testing devices has influenced many branches of Polish industry to make the magnetic testing of wire ropes obligatory. Polish passenger ropeways were the first to introduce obligatory magnetic testing of ropes in 1974. At the end of the 1970's the Polish mining regulations required periodic magnetic non-destructive testing of winding ropes and a Branch Standard, BN/79/5021/09, was subsequently issued covering magnetic testing of these ropes.

The instruments employed in Poland for testing ropes use the method of a static magnetic field from powerful permanent magnets to magnetize the rope, the principles of operation of which are shown in Fig 1 (Kawecki and Hansel (2), Hansel (3, 4, 5), and Kawecki and Lankosz (6)). Information relating to rope conditions are picked up by sensors inside the detecting head. The voltage signal received from the sensors is directly proportional to the change of the cross-sectional area of the rope (Fig 2 and Fig 3). Until recently, the Polish testing instruments used double inductive sensors. Such a system was recognized to be the best one for measuring the majority of the defects, because it could detect the position of defects and furnished sufficient information to calculate the size of defects on either the outer surface or within the rope.

The magnitude of single or clustered defects, U, can be computed using the following formula:

$$U = \frac{U_\phi}{k_s \cdot k_\rho \cdot k_v}$$

where: U_ϕ – standard defect
k_s – factor of gap between the ends of a broken wire
k_ρ – factor of position of defect in rope
k_v – factor of rope speed

The values U_ϕ, k_s, k_ρ and k_v are obtained from the measurements of the signal pulse and from the calibration relationships for the instrument, according to the method developed at the University of Mining and Metallurgy in Kraków. That method has been issued in the form of a manual.

At present, wherever it is possible, Hall induction sensors are used. They possess all the qualities of the induction sensors and can also detect and measure gradual changes of rope cross-section which occur over lengths of the rope. The magnitude of defects such as broken wires, corrosion pits can be calculated according to the method described above, using the signal recorded from the induction sensors. The magnitude of defects, like those caused by advanced corrosion or abrasion can be computed, using the Hall sensor signal, from the formula:

$$U = k . A$$

where: A   –   amplitude of signal recorded
         k   –   defectorgraph processing constant

Wherever high accuracy is needed for the measurement of loss of rope strength, Δ, it may be calculated using the formula:

$$\Delta = f(a) . U$$

where: f(a)   –   is the function, determined by experiment, between the drop of the breaking load (of the whole rope) and its defects
         U   –   defect, calculated in the way described above.

The function f(a) is valid for a given construction and diameter of rope operating in certain conditions.

More than ten detecting heads have been developed which use either inductive or the Hall inductive sensors. The main parameters of the heads, including details of sensors, rope diameter capability and recommended applications for usage are set out in Table 1. From the description given in Table 1 the GP-1, GP-2S and GP-2SR heads are especially recommended for winding ropes.

The magnetic testing instruments developed in Poland have special electronic devices and recorders adapted for use with the detecting heads. At present, two types of dedicated instruments are produced:

(i)   the defectographs - record the direct or processed signals from the sensors, from which it is possible to calculate, with relative accuracy, the magnitude of the defects according to the methods presented; and,

(ii)   the defectoscopes - automatically analyse the signals, adding up the defects and comparing them with previously assumed levels of rope deterioration. They also provide a light or sound signal when a pre-selected level of deterioration has been reached.

The defectoscopes are used for rough control of ropes by personnel with lower rope inspection qualifications. The main parameters of the instruments for use with the measuring heads presently manufactured are set out in Table 2. Figure 2 shows a selection of the range of measuring heads and associated signal processing equipment developed and manufactured in Poland.

ORGANISATION OF MAGNETIC TESTING OF WIRE ROPE IN POLAND AND RELATED STATUTORY REGULATIONS AND STANDARDS

In Poland there are two kinds of legal acts which are concerned with the magnetic testing of wire ropes:

(i)   detailed regulations which impose the obligation of periodic wire rope testing on appropriate branches of industry (e.g. ropeways, mining etc.); and,

(ii)   standards which specify the ways and methods of carrying out the magnetic testing of wire ropes for specific installations and set out the way to interpret the test results.

The magnetic testing of wire ropes used in ropeways and mining hoist installatios has only recently become obligatory. Regular magnetic testing of wire ropes used in ropeways commended in 1948 ((1), (6)).

The statutory requirement for periodic magnetic testing was introduced only in 1974 following the issuing of "Technical Regulations Concerning Ropeways Maintenance and Exploitation". These regulations require the operators to conduct magnetic inspection of all kinds of ropes with the exception of tension (counterweight) ropes, at least once in a year. The ropes must be tested magnetically for the first time just after having been installed. Despite the positive results arising from the magnetic inspection trials of mine ropes carried out between the years 1948 to 1950, it took until 1963 before the magnetic methods were introduced into the Polish mining industry.

Development of the magnetic equipment and magnetic testing methods ensured that the testing of mine hoisting rope using this technique became obligatory in 1979. The magnetic inspections of wire ropes performed up to 1979 were performed as development exercises to increase the accuracy of rope testing in special cases.

Regulations requiring periodic magnetic inspection of hoisting, guide, fender and balance ropes were introduced in the "Detail regulations relating to mine operational and deposit economy in underground ore mines" (for use in Polish copper, zinc and lead mines). These regulations specify that:

(i)   Guide and fender ropes should be inspected magnetically once in the first three months of service and then periodically tested at least once every two years;

(ii)   for hoisting ropes these times are shorter and equal to two weeks and six months respectively; and,

(iii)   ropes for winding installations with low intensity of hoisting and a not very aggressive shaft environment must be tested at least once every 12 months, whilst for balance ropes the admissible time between inspections is three years.

The "Detail regulations relating to mine operation and deposit economy in underground mining plants winning hard and brown coal" issued in 1980 impose rgulations for periodic magnetic inspection of ropes in col mines. Hoisting ropes are required to be inspected magnetically once in the first month of service and then at least once every six months of service. The Branch Standard BN/79/5021/09 "Round Mine Ropes. Determination of the Degree of Wear by the Magnetic Method" was issued in 1972 to unify the way of carrying out magnetic testings. Recently this standard came into force in Poland and includes a detailed description of the methods of use for non-destructive testing of ropes and also the ways of calculating rope wear on the basis of the magnetic testings.

The periodic magnetic inspections required by the Polish regulations referred to here are carried out by particular competent departments. The magnetic inspection of all aerial ropeway ropes are conducted by the Ropeway District Technical Supervision Department in Kraków. Periodic rope inspections in hard coal mines are conducted by the Centres of Measures and Automation existing in the hard coal mining companies and also by the Central Testing Laboratory in Myslowice. The Wire Rope and Suspension Gear Laboratory of the Copper Mining-Metallurgic Plant in Lublin, services all copper mines situated in the Lower Silesia.

The Interbranch Laboratory for Wire Rope Testing at the University of Mining and Metallurgy in Kraków is the main centre in the field of wire rope magnetic testing. The measuring instruments of ropes and the methods of measuring and calculating the degree of rope wear and the weakening of wire ropes for different installations and different environmental conditions were developed at the Interbranch Laboratory. The Interbranch Laboratory has also developed the regulations and standards relating to the non-destructive testing of ropes which are now in force in Poland. For many years, the Interbranch Laboratory has trained rope NDT specialists through post-graduate studies and courses which cover use of equipment and methods of calculating the degree of rope wear on the basis of results obtained using the Polish NDT devices. About 250 specialists from Poland have completed post-graduate courses on the "Exploitation of Wire Ropes". The Interbranch Laboratory also trains foreign specialists and users of the Polish NDT equipment. More than 30 specialists from the UK, France, USA, West Germany, Bulgaria and Rumania have completed these courses.

ECONOMIC AND OPERATIONAL EFFECTS OF ROPE NDT

The development and use of more accurate magnetic testing methods has enabled industry to extend the service life of ropes assessed in accordance with the regulations as well as improving the reliability and safety of the rope transport installations.

A detailed analysis of the effects of magnetic rope testings performed in Polish industry has not been made, however the following examples of magnetic inspections serve to illustrate some of the beneficial effects. The most significant achievement using magnetic testing was the service life extension of four track ropes of the Kasprowy Wierch Ropeway. As a direct result of the periodic magnetic testings of the ropes, which were carried out from 1948, the service life of the first set of track ropes (Kasprowy Wierch Ropeway was build in 1936) was extended to 32 – 34 years (2), (6)).

Each year in Poland the research centres perform a combined number of about 3,000 expert magnetic inspections of mine ropes, especially hoisting ones. The combined extension in service life for the ropes which are inspected magnetically can be estimated to be about 4,000 – 5,000 months each year. This brings about substantial economic savings due to lower rope wear and reduction of installation costs.

In addition to developing new measuring instruments, research methods and investigation of wear and discard criteria for ropes, the Interbranch Laboratory also performs 150 expert magnetic testings of ropes operating in different kinds of installations in which the ropes have not been previously inspected. In 1987 the same naval installation on which magnetic rope testings were performed included: trawling ropes, guy ropes of TV aerial masts, drilling ropes, excavator ropes and flat rubber coated tail ropes etc.

It is estimated that, on average, the service life of ropes magnetically inspected by the Interbranch Laboratory increased by about 1.4 to 1.6 times, in comparison to that determined only on the basis of visual inspections. An example which illustrates this point is one of the prototype sections of a flat rubber coated tail rope at Wieczorek Coal Mine in Katowice which is magnetically inspected every six months and has now been inservice for ten years (Hansel (7)).

DEVELOPMENT TRENDS OF WIRE ROPE NDT EQUIPMENT

The recorders and signal analysers manufactured are used exclusively with the detecting heads. Accordingly some special features have been incorporated which facilitate testing, such as compensation of the speed effect on the signal output trace, and the proportional drive of the chart in relation to the rope speed. In recent years some variations to the regular equipment have been developed. One such variant is the multi-channel instrument shown in Figure 5 for recording the diagnostic signals from mine ropes (Hansel and Lankosz (8)). The instrument is used for testing of winding ropes, guide ropes, rubber coated flat tail ropes, and fender ropes. It includes all the assemblies presently used in the defectographs. In addition to the applications men-tioned above, this instrument is used in connection with rope load sensors and with acceleration sensors for diagnostic testing of the condition of guides in mine shafts, and of other elements in the winding gear. There is a multi-channel magnetic recording of the output signals. This leads to a new dustproof and splashproof version of the instrument which also made it possible to numerically process the recorded signals by computer.

Changes have been made in the detecting heads at the same time as improvements in the recorders and analysers have been introduced. The aim of these changes is to make them lighter and to improve their metrological properties. Two of the new measuring heads, the GP-2SRH and GP-8k may be seen as examples of these changes. The first one has a guide roller for the rope, is air-tight and is designed for testing guide and fender ropes, which operate in very difficult conditions (water, aggressive dust etc.)

Although the head has been made air and water tight its weight is about 10% lower than that of the GP-2S head (listed in Table 1) and also the accuracy of measurements on 50 to 60 mm ropes, whose diameters are within the upper range of that head, has been increased. The other modernized head, the GP-8k, is also waterproof and has been designed for testing ruber coated flat tail ropes, incorporating calibrating ferromagnetic elements within the head. This head can operate with the multi-channel diagnostic instrument and may also be used separately since it has a built-in electronic analyser. When used on its own, the head gives signals if the deterioration of the rope has exceeded its permissible level. Analysis of progressive weakening of the rope is made by a continuous comparison of the signal in proportion to a known defect signal coming from the calibrating ferromagnetic element vulcanized inside rubber.

For many years now, work at the Interbranch Laboratory for Wire Rope Testing has been carried out on the development of wire rope non-destructive testing equipment and associated quantitative assessment of the degree of rope wear. This work has extended the range of applications in which these devices may be practically used, in addition to the ropes of mine winders and ropeways that are presently tested magnetically. Results obtained from this work show that it is possible and purposeful to use these NDT devices to inspect ropes in the following applications:

(i)   elevator ropes (Kawecki and Hansel (2) and Kawecki and Lankosc (6));

(ii)   ropes operating in marine environment such as trawling ropes (Hansel and Cholewa (9));

(iii)   ropes used on large excavator machinery as shown in Fig 6, for which a short length of typical output trace indicating types of damage is shown in Fig 7 (Hansel and others (10));

(iv)   flat rubber coated tail ropes such as the one shown in Fig 8, using the GP-8 head shown in Fig 9 from which a typical output trace is shown in Fig 10 (Hansel (7));

(v)   guy ropes of TV aerial masts (results not published);

(vi)   drilling ropes (results not published); and,

(vii)   mooring ropes on offshore platforms (results not published).

CONCLUSIONS

In conclusion, the points discussed in this paper may be summarised as follows:

(i)   the instruments for magnetic non-destructive testing of wire ropes have been developed which cover the whole range of rope diameters used in Poland;

(ii)   NDT methods using these devices have been developed for the quantitative assessment of wire rope wear and damage;

(iii)   a group of 250 specialists have been trained in Poland at the post-graduate courses on how to operate the magnetic testing equipment;

(iv)   defectographs, defectoscopes and measuring heads of the various types developed have been produced in forms suitable for both Polish and foreign users;

(v)   a group of foreign specialists have been trained at the Interbranch Laboratory in the operation of the magnetic NDT equipment and the interpretation of the results.

REFERENCES

(1)   Kawecki, Z, and Stachurski, J, "Non-Desctructive Magnetic Testing of Steel Ropes", Wydawnictwo Slask, Katowice, 1969.

(2)   Kawecki, Z, and Hansel, J, "Development and Future Perspective of Magnetic Testing of Steel Wire Ropes", Internationales Colloquium 150 Jahre Drahtseil, Technische Akademie Esslingen, 1984, pp 15.1-15.15.

(3)   Hansel, J, "Problems of a Quantitative Assessment of Safety and Reliability of Wire Ropes", Proc. International Lift Symposium on Safety and Reliability, International Congrescentrum RAI Amsterdam, 1984, pp 115-124.

(4)   Hansel, J, "Some Works on Fatigue Life and Reliability Diagnostic of Wire Rope", Bulletin 47 OIPEEC, 1984, pp 9-31.

(5)   Hansel, J, "Results of Some Selected Works on Shaft Hoisting at the University of Mining and Metallurgy in Kraków", Kwartalnik "Mechanika", Wyd. AGH Vol 4, 1985, pp 5-30.

(6)   Kawecki, Z, and Lankosz, L, "Selected Problems of the Development of Polish Instruments for Magnetic Defectoscopy of Wire Ropes", Kwartalnik "Mechanika", Wyd. AGH Vol 4, 1985, pp 31-45.

(7)   Hansel, J, "Rubber Coated Flat Tail Ropes for Mine Hoists", International Conference on Hoisting of Men, Materials and Minerals, The Canadian Institute of Mining and Minerals, Toronto, 1988, Vol 2, pp 1115-1131.

(8)   Hansel, J, and Lankosz, L, "Magnetic Testing of Winding Ropes", International Conference on Hoisting of Men, Materials and Minerals, The Canadian Institute of Mining and Minerals Toronto, 1988, Vol 2, pp 1285-1294.

(9)   Hansel, J, and Cholewa, W, "Determination of Wear of Wire Ropes Operating in Sea Water Conditions", Morski Instytut Rybacki, Gdynia, 1980, pp 195-207.

(10)   Hansel, K, and others, A, "Non-Destructive Testing of Wire Ropes on Surface Mining Equipment", The International Journal of Exploring, Developing, Operating, Managing Surface Mines, Trans Tech Publications 1-3, 1987, pp 277-281.

TABLE 1 Main Parameters of the Polish Detecting Heads

Head Type	Mass (kg)	Sensor Type	Sensor Diameter (mm)	Range of Rope Diameters (mm)	Recommended Usage
GP–1	66.0	CI–1 or CHI–1	100 and 130 100,145,160	30–85	mine hoists, aerial ropeways
GP–2	46.0	CI–1 or CHI–2	80 and 115 80,125,138	10–60	ropeway track ropes (asymmetrical head)
GP–2S	55.0	CI–2S or CHI–2	80 and 115	10–65	mine hoists, (symmetric head)
GP–2SR	60.0	CI–2S or CHI–2	80 and 115 80,125,138	10–60	rope testing control and same as GP-2
GP–3	16.0	CI–3 or CIb–3 or CHI–3	50 45 and 65 50 and 50	10–35	haulage ropes for ropeways, mine haulage, drill rigs
GP–3A	11.7	CI–3	50	10–35	Same as GP-3
GP–3R	14.0	CI–3	50	10–35	Same as GP-3
GP–4	6.3	CI–4	35	10–26	Passenger and freight elevators and same as GP-3
GP–5	5.0	CI–5	20	10–15	Same as GP-4
GP–6–6	12.5	CI–6–6	20	10–14	
GP–6–4	8.5	CI–6–4	20	10–14	multi-rope passenger freight elevators
GP–8 GP–8k	65.0	CI–8		20–40 rope thickness	rubber coated flat tail ropes
GP–9		CI–9			wire rope reinforced conveyor belts (in preparation)

TABLE 2 Main Parameters of Polish Defectoscopes and Defectographs

Features of Device	Defectograph/Defectoscope Type andManufacturer		
	MD 12h Mera-Ster	DLS ZEG Tychy	MD 10P Mera-Ster
Overall Dimensions (mm)	415 x 337 x 172	540 x 282 x 260	455 x 185 x 302
Weight (kg)	12.5	12.5	8
Power Reqirement	220V at 50 Hz	220V at 50 Hz or 12V DC	220V at 50Hz
Speed Range of Rope (m/s)	0.1–3.0	0.1–3.0	0.2–5.0
Speed Compensation Range (m/s)	0.1–3.0	0.25–3.0	No Signal Recording Counting of Defects Based on Pre-set Signal Thresholds From a Known Length of Rope Five Levels of Wear Signalling: If One of the Levels is Exceeded, a Sound or Light Signals
Number of Recording Channels	3	3	
Form of Signal Recorded	Pulse, Integrated and Hall Signal	Pulse, Integrated and Hall Signal	
Terminal for Hall Sensor by PH Adaptor	Two Hall Adapors Built-in	Yes	
Recording Tape Feed	Proportional to Rope Length or Time Dependent at 1, 5 & 20 m/s	Proportional to Rope Length or Time Dependent at 2.5, 5, 10 & 20 m/s	
Recording Details	Thermic 1, Half to Third of Full Sensitivity	Thermic 100, with 50, 25, 10 & 2.5mV/cm	
Accessories	Paint Spray at Defect Locations	12V DC Power Supply	Printer, Paint Spray at Locations Where Pre-set Levels of Wear Exceeded

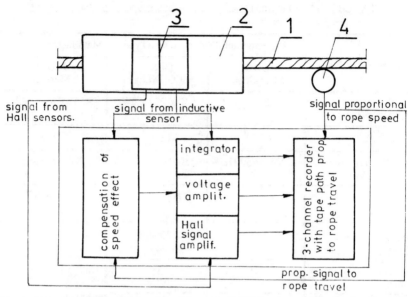

Fig. 1   Principle of Operation of the Magnetic NDT Device with Inductive Sensors for Testing Wire Ropes

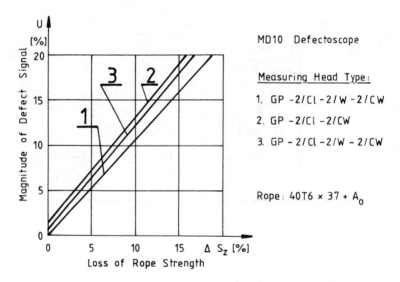

Fig. 2   Defectoscope Signal Magnitude Versus Actual Rope Weakening, S_z

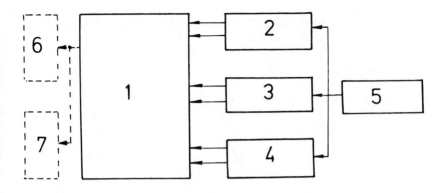

1 - six channel magnetic recorder
2 - measuring head,
3 - acceleration sensors,
4 - load sensors,

5 - feed 220 V, 50- 60 Hz or
    12 V DC,
6 - paper tape recorder,
7 - personal computer.

Fig. 5   Block Diagram for the Recently Developed Diagnostic Testing Equipment for
Mine Shaft Winding Gear Elements

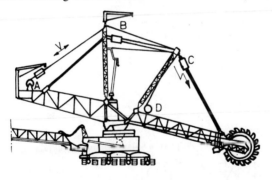

A = Rope measuring point at the drum
B = Rope measuring point at the fixed pulley blocks
    on the successive rope branches
C = Point of monting the head on the stationary rope
D = Location of moveable head

Fig. 6   Rope Reeving Diagram for the SchRs6300 Excavator, Indicating Locations
Where the NDT Device may be Attached for Inspecting the Ropes

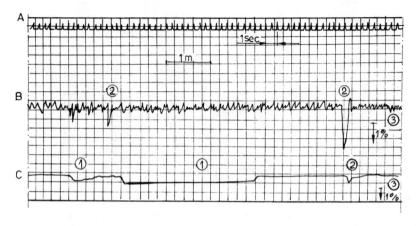

A = Time marker
B = Induction sensor signal
C = Hall sensor signal

1 = Missing wire
2 = Broken wire
3 = Proportional metal loss of rope

Fig. 7   Section of a Defectogram from one of the SchRs6300 Excavator 40T6x37+A_o
Lifting Ropes

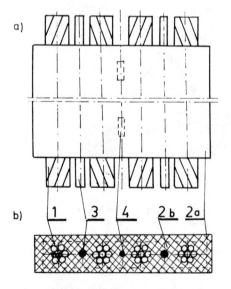

a / general view of rope
b/ cross section of rope

1 - round wire ropes
2- rubber
3- communication lead
4- calibrating element

Fig. 8 Rubber Coated Flat Tail Rope

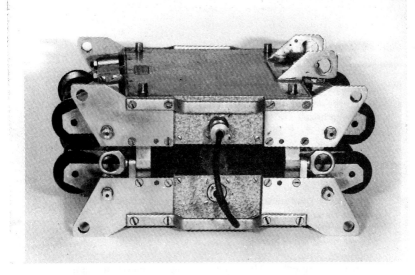

Fig. 9   GP-8 NDT Measuring Head for Testing Rubber Coated Flat Tail Ropes

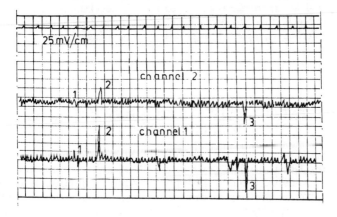

1 - 5 mm dia ball, 2 - 5 mm dia, 8 mm long wi re,
3 - loss of ferromagnetic cross sectional area of rope.

Fig. 10   DLS-Defectograph Record Using the GP-8 Head, Indicating Elements
Detected

NEW DEVELOPMENTS IN AND APPLICATIONS OF WIRE ROPE NDT EQUIPMENT FROM WBK–SEILPRÜFSTELLE

D. FUCHS AND R. SCHRODER

According to existing regulations, winding ropes in the German mining industry are subject to regular visual inspection and non-destructive testing. Starting as early as 1931, WBK-Seilprüfstelle has been developing non-destructive testing devices using the stray flux method. This method is mainly suitable for the detection of outer and inner wire breaks, whereas it is limited in detecting other types of rope damage, such as loss of metallic area by corrosion or wear. These devices have been successfully used for testing winding ropes as well as many other kinds of running ropes, cableways and bridge strands. More recently, to overcome the deficiencies of the stray flux method, WBK-Seilprüfstelle have developed a new type of rope testing device containing three measuring circuits: stray flux, magnetic flux and diameter measurement. By combining these methods to supplement visual inspection, a much more comprehensive assessment of damage to ropes becomes possible. These expectations are confirmed by practical experience obtained so far. A novel application of the combined stray flux and magnetic flux method for inpecting wire reinforced conveyor belts is providing encouraging results.

REGULATIONS GOVERNING THE IMPLEMENTATION OF NON-DESTRUCTIVE ROPE TESTS

Regular testing of winding ropes is compulsory in the German mining industry. Relevant regulations are laid down in the BVOS (1,2). To conform with these regulations non-destructive testing has proved to be an indispensable tool to support visual inspection in assessing the damage condition of wire ropes. According to the inspection findings obtained, a limited interval of further use of the rope may be specified by the expert in charge. In particular the interval is dependent on a careful consideration of the established rope condition and its operating conditions, as well as the operational life elapsed. In the case of high duty winding installations, useful life of the ropes may be limited to less than one year or extend to more than three years.

WBK–Seilprüfstelle, Institut fur Fordertechnik und Werkstoffkunde
Dinnendahlstrasse 9, D-4630 Bochum 1, Federal Republik of Germany

Accordingly, the initial intervals between non-destructive testings are set to approximately three months, whereas towards the end of rope life the intervals may be cut down even to less than four weeks.

DESCRIPTION OF THE STRAY FLUX METHOD USED BY WBK–SEILPRUFSTELLE

WBK-Seilprüfstelle started developing non-destuctive testing devices as early as 1931. The basic concept of the stray flux method has been maintained ever since: the examined rope is magnetized to saturation by means of a static magnetic field. Stray fluxes are generated by both external and internal damages associated with abrupt changes in cross-sections; these stray fluxes will, in turn, generate electric voltages in detecting coils as eith the rope or the testing device is moved (Fig 1). The stray flux method is ideally suited for identifying outer and inner wire breaks. Corrosion pits will also give rise to stray fluxes which generate characteristic responses on the signal output trace.

As time advanced the handling of the testing devices and the comprehensiveness of the signal outputs were improved. The present day devices can be characterized as follows:

(i) Rope magnetization is brought about by ALNICO permanent magnets.

(ii) The detecting coils for stray flux measurement are laid out as so-called differential coils. Four of them surround the rope doubly thus permitting some fault location (Fig 2: array of the differential coils and diagram showing the 4 individual traces). Due to partial overlapping of the differential coils one fault will always be identified by at least two coils - a more substantial fault even by three or four.

(iii) Amplification is adjusted in such a way that the display becomes independent of the rope running speed through the testing device.

(iv) Diagram advance has been linked to the speed at which the rope passes through the testing device so that 1 m of rope length will, no matter what speed, comply to a set length of diagram.

(v) 4 magnetic sensing heads cover a rope diameter range between 30 mm and 175 mm.

WBK-Seilprüfstelle uses these devices to carry out a wide variety of tests on running ropes e.g. of winding equipment, cableways, cranes, on ropes of offshore equipment, as well as on standing ropes, such as bridge ropes, guy ropes on transmission towers and stacks.

A series of tests carried out under contract for comparing the performance of various NDT devices (3), which showed that the WBK-Seilprüfstelle stray flux measuring method provides a very high resolution sensitivity in detecting wire breaks independent of the kind of rope construction.

LIMITATIONS OF THE STRAY FLUX METHOD

In addition to outer and inner wire breaks, corrosion and wear are also major factors contributing to critical rope conditions. It is at this point that the stray flux methd is bounded by its physical limitations. Whenever the metallic area of a rope is reduced by corrosion, the output diagram will not give any indication of the amount of loss, as it is exclusively the shape and depth of corrosion pits which influence the magnitude of the signal. For the same reasons metallic area loss by wear will not be detected by stray flux measurement.

To put it more generally: the stray flux method is not capable of identifying any metallic area loss varying gradually over a significant length of rope.

Other conventional devices used for non-destructive rope testing are similarly inappropriate for identifying with any certainty most other rope defects which restrict the operating condition of a rope e.g. kinks and loss of diameter.

NEW NON-DESTRUCTIVE ROPE TESTING DEVICE DEVELOPED BY WBK–SEILPRUFSTELLE

Research performed by WBK-Seilprüfstelle found that it is only by simultaneous application of different non-destructive testing methods which enables those rope conditions that may develop into critical situations, to be detected with certainty. Consequently a new rope testing device was conceived and constructed which includes three measuring circuits:

(i)   stray flux measurement;

(ii)   magnetic flux measurement; and,

(iii) optical diameter measurement.

Combining the three measuring circuits to supplement visual inspection results in a substantially improved tool to assess more comprehensively the momentary condition of a rope and its expected future behaviour with due consideration of rope loads.

The new rope testing device consists of a magnetic sensing head containing the two magnetic measuring circuits for stray flux and magnetic flux measurement, and an optical diameter measuring head and separate evaluation electronics including chart recorder (Fig 3). The static magnetic fields are generated by rare earth permanent magnets. This combines favourable dimensions and weights with the capability to saturate magnetically even ropes of large diameter. Two magnetic sensing heads suffice to examine ropes of diameters between 30 mm and 90 mm have been developed. A special version of the magnetic sensing head has been designed for non-destructive underwater testing e.g. of the mooring ropes of offshore drilling platforms.

The measuring circuit for stray flux measurement was adopted, unmodified, from the conventional WBK-Seilprüfstelle devices which were of proven ability.

For magnetic flux measurement a detecting coil version was selected following comparative experiments with Hall effect devices. A number of alternatives were considered for arranging the magnetic flux detecting coil in the sensing head, a coil surrounding the rope and located between the stray flux coils turned out to be particularly suitable (Fig 4). For ease of handling, a flat line comprising 12 parallel cores was selected, which is wound some 12 to 15 times on a coil form around the rope, so that the required number of windings is completed in very short time. The different cores are then put in series via a plug. The measuring voltage induced in the coil is passed to an electronic integrator. The output signal of the integrator is proportional to the change in metallic area running through the magnetic sensing head.

Experiments have confirmed that the change in signal from the magnetic flux measuring circuit is proportional to the amount of variation in metallic area of the rope. The measured change in metallic area is independent of whether it is situated at the inside or at the outside of the rope's cross-section.

The measuring concept, however, allows detection of change in metallic area relative to some reference cross-section only. A sufficiently accurate calibration is achieved when a certain number of wires are introduced in the magnetic sensing head mounted to the rope, in order to simulate metallic area change.

Detailed checking of the accuracy of metallic area measurements, obtained from ropes tested in service is laborious. Whilst the rope testing device can easily be set to sensitivity sufficient to allow diagram readings of less than 0.1% of metallic area changes, one should, however, consider measuring sensitivity separately from measuring acuracy. Measuring accuracy of the WBK equipment was checked, both in laboratory tests, and also on sections of discarded winding ropes which exhibited sizeable corrosion-induced alterations of their metallic area over short lengths. That loss of metallic area was determined first by the rope testing device. The ropes were then unlaid and the individual wire diameters checked and from which loss in the metallic area was calculated. Calculations yielded an average discrepancy against magnetic flux measurement of between 0.5% and 1% of the metallic area. The values found from measurement of metallic area were always higher than that defined by checking the diameter of single wires. This can be explained by the fact that wire surfaces were always roughened by corrosion pits. When checking wire diameters the metallic area loss due to missing material in the corrosion pits was not onsidered. The outcome of these experiments showed that the acuracy of the magnetic flux circuit is entirely sufficient for the safe assessment of rope condition, particularly since conversion of loss of metallic area into breaking load loss has to be left to expert judgement anyway.

Rope diameter is measured by means of an optical non-contact laser scanning system. It has been designed for use mainly on running ropes. The scanning rate had to be substantially increased over conventional laser scanning systems in order to obtain an accurate scanning profile of the rope with its successive bulges and reductions in shape. The diameter measuring device covers rope diameters over the entire examined length and thereby detects all faults reflected by changes in diameter. Direct contact between strands, for example will be detected first by a corresponding reduction in diameter.

EXAMPLES OF ROPE EXAMINATIONS IN SHAFT-WINDING INSTALLATIONS

To illustrate the progress made through the newly developed testing device the following two examples will describe some results from measurements on winding ropes of shaft-winding systems (details are set out in Appendix 1). The effect of wire breaks is less apparent in these examples as they have been selected particularly to illustrate the type of information obtained from the magnetic flux and the diameter measurement. However wire breaks may be the dominating type of damage in other cases, such as shown in Fig 2.

The first example covers a single-rope installation in a shaft with a prevailing corrosive atmosphere. The status of the three-layer oval strand rope of 52 mm rated diameter and 1,077 mm^2 metallic area was characterized by corrosion. The first measurement had been carried out after 70 months of rope operation, by using the new testing device.

Figure 5 illustrates the metallic area profile on a length from 2 m until 900 m above one of the bindings. The most severe loss in metallic area has clearly occurred within the zone passing the pulley during the hoisting acceleration period.

Corrosion attack was particularly severe on the short lengths of rope which - when the hoisting cage stops at the shaft insets - are located at the passages locking the shaft area frm the external atmosphere. The chart on Fig 6 was taken from the short rope length in the zone of acceleration. The traces on the chart represent, from the top: the stray flux signals produced by the four stray flux coils, the added signal of coils 3 and 4, the magnetic flux trace, the roe diameter trace, the distance identification, they do not quantify the pertinent change in metallic area which is obtained exclusively from the magnetic flux measurement. The most significant metallic area loss, which occurs at the 123 m point, amount to approximately 3.7% referred to the initial metallic area. This means a local metallic area loss of 2.6% on a rope length of as short as 6 m. Such loss in metallic area is also reflected by the displayed loss in diameter from 52.5 mm to 52.0 mm.

When the measurement was repeated three months later, visible corrosion had progressed. As can be seen on Fig 7, rope condition worsened particularly over the entire zone of acceleration. Now the most significant metallic area loss amounts to

6.7% and is, again, located at 123 m. Locally, over a length of 6 m, the metallic area is reduced by 4.5% (Fig 8). Regardless of the advanced material loss there is hardly any change in the shape of the stray flux signals. This may be explained by the fact that shape and depth of corrosion pits did not change. Also the rope diameter did not change in comparison to the first measurement.

The second example refers to the 6 stranded ordinary lay rope of a winding installation. The rope has a rated diameter of 59 mm and 1416 mm^2 metallic area. Due to shaft environment and operational conditions the ropes of that installation are discarded, inter alia, for corrosion and wear in the strand gaps because of strand contact.

Figure 9 shows the metallic area and the rope diameter on the entire length of the rope. Both of the lines exhibit a correlation with severe reduction in the zones of acceleration. This particularly applies to the eastern acceleration zone where the measured rope diameter of 54.2 mm is clearly below that diameter where contact between strands commences or, in other words, where the strand gaps will show clear signs of wear at the points of contact between wires. At the same time there is a loss in metallic area of 8% that may be attributed to corrosion and wear. Looking closer at the measuring output, some 5% of that loss may be related to corrosion loss and approximately 3% to wear of the wires at contact points between strands. Reliable assessment of defect situation was possible only from metallic area and diameter measurement.

Figure 10 is the output chart for the length between 97 m and 106 m above the eastern rope binding. The stray flux traces and the metallic area traces are displayed together with two types of diameter traces. One of these shows the primary signal of the laser device with the typical bulges and reductions of shape of a rope. The other trace is the micro-computer processed "envelope-curve" that picks up the maxima of the primary signal for more convenient presentation of diameter changes.

CONCLUSIONS

On the basis of the examples presented and the existing experience of almost 60 years of testing practice at WBK-Seilprüfstelle, the concluding remarks about non-detructive testing of wire ropes may be summarized in brief as follows:

Any possible conclusion from non-destructive rope testing is only as good as the interpretation of the obtained results, which accordingly must be provided by an experienced expert. Practiced this way, non-destructive testing of ropes not only offers the possibility to identify the existing type of damage but also to predict the likely progress of damage up to its critical stage.

OTHER APPLICATIONS

Finally, it may be mentioned, that the test methods developed are suitable for other non-destructive testing applications as well. WBK-Seilprüfstelle has a device under test which has been designed for the non-destructive testing of steel wire reinforced conveyor belts. The unit consists of several stray flux and magnetic flux measuring circuits providing a monitoring of the entire belt width separated in 200 mm wide strips. The testing device is expected to detect developing faults in steel wire reinforced conveyor belts at a very early stage.

REFERENCES

(1)   BVOS, "Bergverordnung des Landesobergamts Nordrhein-Westfalen für Schact- und Schrägförderanlagen (Mine Regulations for Vertical- and Inclined Shaft mining Installations)", Bellmann-Verlag, Dortmund, 20th July 1977.

(2)   "Verwaltungsanweisung des Landesoberbergamts Nordrhein-Westfalen zur BVOS und zu den TAS (Administrative Guidelines for Regulatory (BVOS) and Technical (TAS) Requirements for Vertical- and Inclined Shaft Mining Installations)", Bellman-Verlag, Dortmund, 29th March, 1984.

(3)   Poirier, L., "Non-Destructive Testing of Wire Rope" , Commission for European Community, Mines Safety and Health Commission, Doc. No. 4278/81, Luxembourg, 1981.

APPENDIX 1

1. Features of winding installation and rope design at Minister Stein colliery, shaft 6.

   – Single-rope installation in a main shaft
   – Surface shaft, wet conditions
   – Shaft travel: 912 m
   – Ground-mounted winder with DC drive motor
   – Hoisting cage and counterweight

   – Right-handed three-layer oval strand rope,
     Rated diameter 52 mm
     Tensile grade 1,770 N/mm^2
     Surface finish of wires: heavy galvanisation

   – Rope composition:
     5 * 8 * 1.70 mm diameter (natural core)
     6 * 10 * 1.60 mm diameter (aluminium core)
         14 * 1.87 mm diameter   + natural core
     8 * 12 * 1.74 mm diameter (aluminium core) + filler fibre
         16 * 2.01 mm diameter

2. Features of winding installation and rope design at Schlägel & Eisen colliery, shaft 2.

   – Single-rope winding installation in a main shaft
   – Surface shaft, wet conditions
   – Shaft travel: 1,175 m
   – Ground-mounted winder with asynchronous three-phase induction motor with slip ring motor

   – Hoisting cage and counterweight

   – Right-handed ordinary lay rope
     Rated diameter 59 mm
     Tensile grade 1,770 N/mm^2
     Surface finish of wires: galvanised
   – Rope composition:

	1 * 1.68 mm diameter
	6 * 1.59 mm diameter
	8 * 2.79 mm diameter
Fibre core + 6 *	8 * 2.54 mm diameter
	8 * 1.94 mm diameter
	16 * 2.97 mm diameter

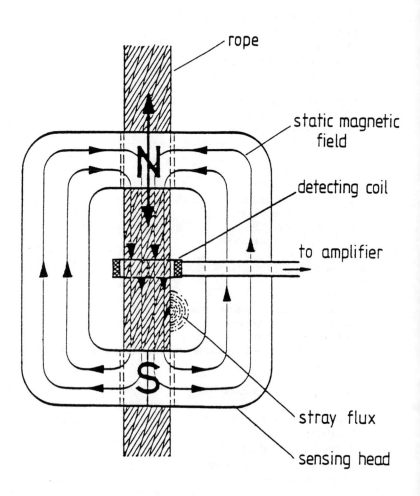

Fig. 1   Principle of magnetic stray flux
measurement

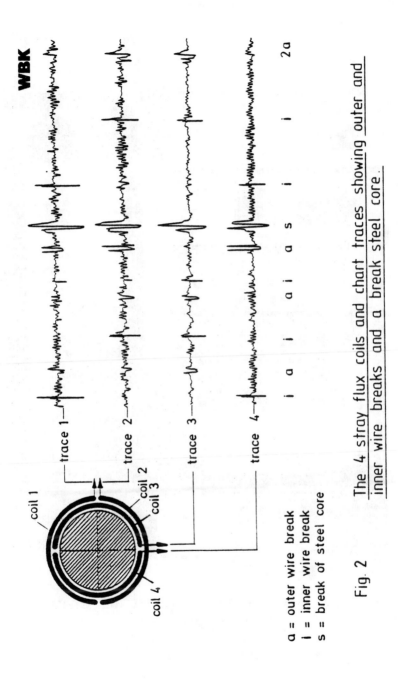

Fig. 2   The 4 stray flux coils and chart traces showing outer and inner wire breaks and a break steel core.

a = outer wire break
i = inner wire break
s = break of steel core

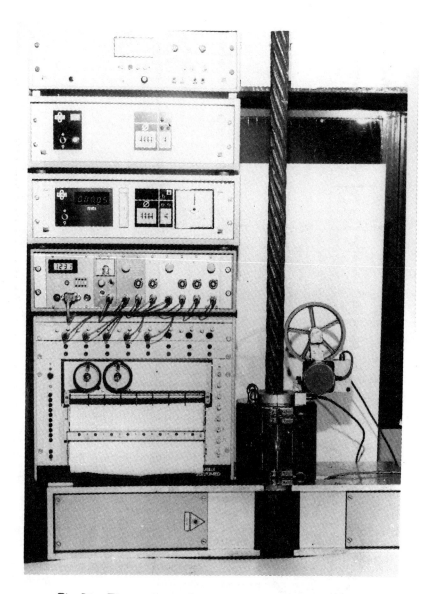

Fig.3 The new wire rope testing device
of WBK Seilprüfstelle

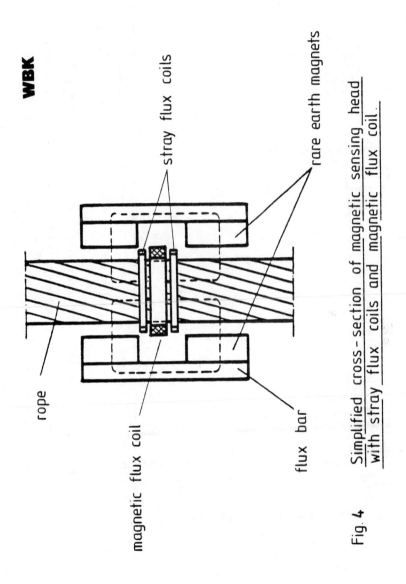

WBK

rope

magnetic flux coil

stray flux coils

flux bar

rare earth magnets

Fig. 4   Simplified cross-section of magnetic sensing head with stray flux coils and magnetic flux coil.

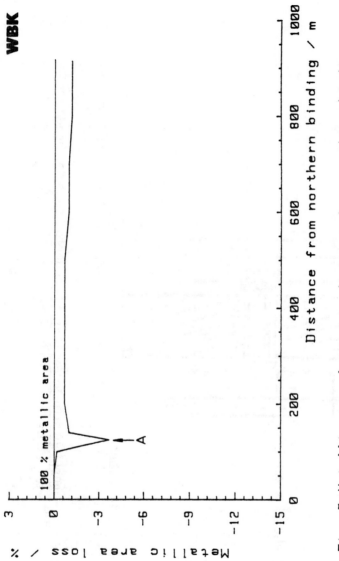

Fig. 5 Metallic area loss over distance from northern binding

3 layer oval strand rope of Minister Stein colliery shaft 6

1. measurement

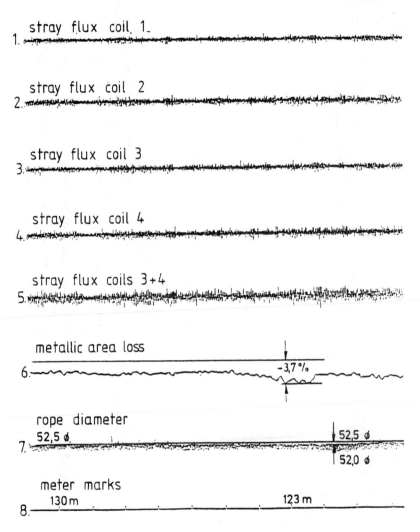

WBK

1. stray flux coil 1

2. stray flux coil 2

3. stray flux coil 3

4. stray flux coil 4

5. stray flux coils 3+4

6. metallic area loss —3,7 %

7. rope diameter 52,5 Ø   52,5 Ø   52,0 Ø

8. meter marks 130 m   123 m

Fig. 6   Field chart of the 3 layer oval strand
          rope of Minister Stein colliery shaft 6
          first measurement-position A in figure 5

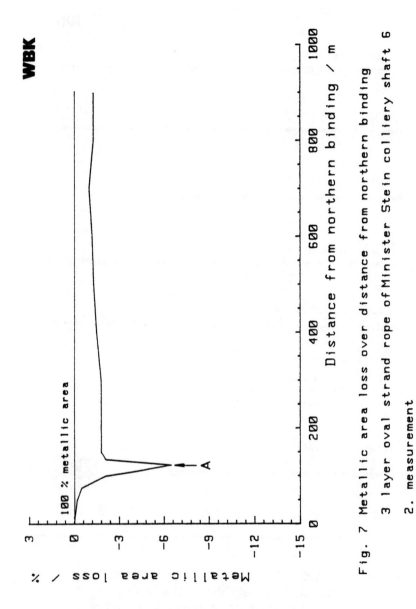

Fig. 7 Metallic area loss over distance from northern binding

3 layer oval strand rope of Minister Stein colliery shaft 6

2. measurement

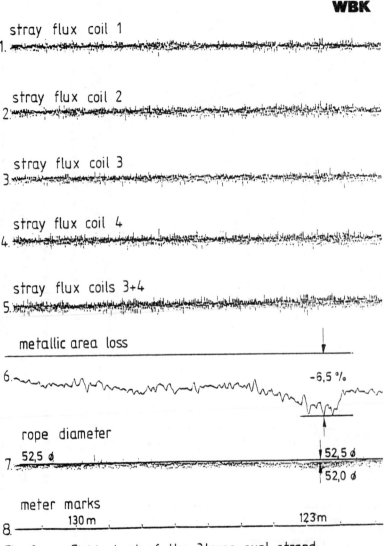

WBK

stray flux coil 1

1.

stray flux coil 2

2.

stray flux coil 3

3.

stray flux coil 4

4.

stray flux coils 3+4

5.

metallic area loss

6.

-6,5 %

rope diameter

7. 52,5 ø

52,5 ø

52,0 ø

meter marks

8.

130 m

123 m

Fig. 8   Field chart of the 3layer oval strand
rope of Minister Stein colliery shaft 6
second measurement - position A in figure 7

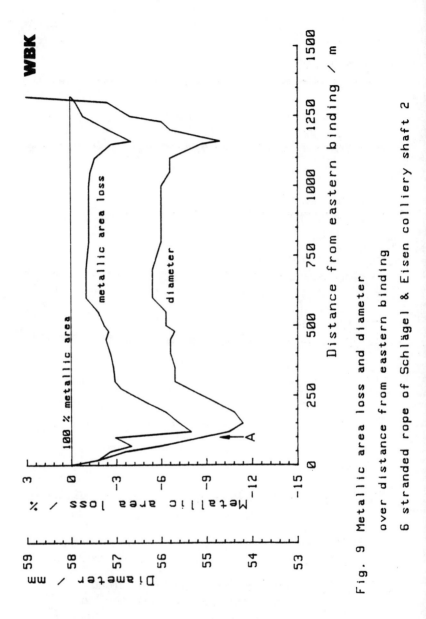

Fig. 9 Metallic area loss and diameter
over distance from eastern binding
6 stranded rope of Schlägel & Eisen colliery shaft 2

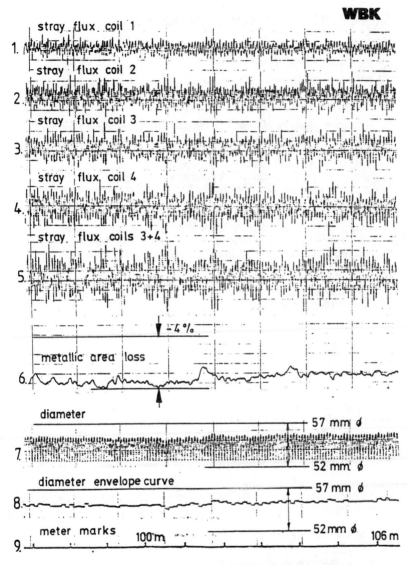

Fig. 10   Field chart of the 6-stranded rope of
           Schlägel & Eisen colliery shaft 2
           - position A in figure 9

THE ACOUSTIC EMISSION OF WIRE ROPE

N F CASEY

This paper describes the development of techniques of monitoring the acoustic emission of wire rope within the laboratory during fatigue testing and presents new results which correlate with changes in wire rope mechanical properties. The objective of this work is to determine the degradation processes which take place in large diameter wire ropes when subjected to tension-tension fatigue. Specific stages during a fatigue test where large amounts of wire break activity take place have been identified. The sources of detectable acoustic emission activity which take place within a wire rope specimen include wire breaks, interwire fretting and emissions from the end connections, in particular the resin cappings. Based on the work carried out by the author and other workers, suggestions have been put forward for possible applications of acoustic emission monitoring of wire rope outside the laboratory.

INTRODUCTION

Since wire ropes suffer from mechanical damage in use and corrosion damage by exposure to the elements, inspection to determine their continued reliability is an important task. The most common form of wire rope inspection is still a visual examination but it is not possible to detect all the faults this way. As a consequence of the problem of inspecting a wire rope thoroughly, rope utilization tends to be conservative.

The parameters under which a wire rope operates vary considerably and it is these parameters or changes in these parameters which can affect the life of a rope. The following significant parameters have been listed by Savill (1).

1   Load and load application

2   Speed - acceleration and deceleration

National Engineering Laboratory, East Kilbride, Glasgow G75 0QU

3   Frequency of operation

4   Load and strength ratio

5   Bending radii

6   Bending

7   Bending frequency

8   Distance between direction changes

9   Abrasion

10   Crushing on drums

11   Fit of rope in sheave or drum grooves

12   Corrosive or dry atmosphere

13   Temperature

14   Maintenance - lubrication, type of lubricant

15   End fittings.

The main forms of rope degradation and causes of failure which result from the conditions under which a rope operates have been given in the Ropeman's Handbook (2) and these are:

1   Wear, both internal and external

2   Corrosion, both internal and external

3   Fatigue

4   Corrosion fatigue

5   Surface embrittlement

6   Accidental damage and distortion, leading to local degradation.

Egan (3), stated that the requirements of inspecting a wire rope include discovering and measuring the degradation, evaluating the inspection data and deciding whether or not to replace the rope. The specification of a suitable non-destructive testing device to meet these requirements has been summarised by Babel (4).

1   The device should be of light weight and easy to operate

2   It should enable the examination of a rope in service without major interruption

3   It should allow attachment to an endless rope

4   The device must not damage the rope

5   It should be able to ascertain the condition of a rope.

At present, the devices which come close to satisfying these inspection requirements are based on magnetic techniques. These devices have been developed to the point where they are routinely reliable and are used in the field to inspect both standing and running ropes.

The acoustic emission method of inspection has the potential to satisfy the requirements for a suitable non-destructive test device; however, the rope needs to be monitored continuously because, unlike most other techniques of non-destructive testing, acoustic emission detects events as they happen.

Acoustic emission can be defined as transient elastic (or stress) waves which are generated by the rapid release of energy within a material. The method relies on the application of a stress in order that defects can emit the resulting stress waves as they grow. When the acoustic emissions (or stress waves) reach the surface of the material being examined, the small displacements they produce are detected by piezoelectric transducers and converted into electrical signals. These transduced acoustic emission signals are then amplified, conditioned, recorded and finally analysed.

PREVIOUS WORK

Acoustic emission monitoring techniques have been in use for about 20 years and in the context of this time period only limited work has been carried out to evaluate its suitability for monitoring the condition of wire rope. Early workers, Laura and others (5,6), were successful in using accelerometers clamped to 10 mm (3/8 in) diameter wire rope, of various constructions and length, to detect wire breaks and warn of impending failure during rising load tests. Their work also showed that wire breaks detected before failure were 15-20 dB above background noise.

Harris and Dunegan (7) claimed that, as a result of the more sensitive Dunegan-Endevco 3000 series equipment, ample warning of impending failure was possible during both rising load and tensile fatigue tests carried out on 6 x 19 rope samples 6 mm (0.25 in) diameter and 137 mm (5.5 in) long. Their overall conclusion was that acoustic emission techniques provide a sensitive means of detecting the structural integrity of wire rope.

Work carried out by Bamberger and Robert (8) led to the development of a particular method for detecting and localising failures of constituent wires. Trial experiments involved loading samples of 93-wire strand 52 mm diameter and 200 m long. Ten accelerometers were attached to each strand thus allowing both the velocity of propagation and subsequent loss in amplitude of the signals resulting from wire breaks to be determined.

Fritz and others (9) carried out experimental development of a prototype wire break detector which was produced to monitor wire ropes during fatigue testing. In addition to testing in order to obtain correlations between recorded events and wire breaks, the investigators also carried out tests to determine the resonant frequencies of the experimental set-up including the test machine, specimen length, end fitting length, rope construction and diameter. They concluded from this work that the dominant resonant frequency excited by a wire failure consists of flexural vibration of the tubular end fittings. This work implied that the end fitting should be considered as an integral part of the wire break detector design and the frequency range of the instrument be centred around 9 kHz.

Hanzawa and others (10) produced a wire break detection system of their own design which was capable of locating wire breaks using time of arrival techniques. The instrument was subsequently used in a test programme to investigate the factors which influence the fatigue strength of wire rope. Their test programme included the fatigue testing of 20 hanger ropes and 25 mooring ropes; all of 50 mm diameter and between 700 and 1810 mm in length. Dividing the number of detected breakages by the actual number of wire breaks for each test conducted they achieved detection rates between 30 and 100 per cent. The greater the number of wire breaks the lower the detection rate.

Extensive research into the evaluation of wire ropes using acoustic emission monitoring was carried out at University College Cardiff in the period 1980 to 1987. The work, some of which formed part of the SERC/MTD wire rope research programme, was under the supervision of Dr J L Taylor and resulted in PhD theses by Casey (11) and Holford (12), together with several published papers by Casey and others (13-19). Most of the work was carried out on small diameter ropes subjected either to static loading or tension-tension fatigue; however, tests were carried out using large diameter ropes and a limited amount of work was carried out under bending over sheave conditions referred to in Sections 3 and 4 respectively of this paper. In the remainder of the present section some of the main findings of the work carried out at Cardiff using small diameter ropes will be described.

After carrying out initial experiments into the acoustic emission monitoring of individual rope wires, it was concluded that the only practical way of monitoring wire ropes was to detect the failure of constituent wires. This approach was in common with most of the other workers in this field and a programme of work was set out using 12 mm diameter six-strand rope with an independent wire rope core.

Early work using a Dunegan-Endevco 3000 series acoustic emission monitoring system revealed, under cyclic loading conditions, that a one-to-one correlation could be obtained between wire breaks and acoustic-emission events of amplitude equal to or greater than 80 dB; these signal amplitude values being well above the background noise levels. Other work showed that outer wire breaks could be detected over distances of 29.5 m in ropes subjected to static loading. For each test conducted notches were filed into the wires at a given distance from the transducer, the ropes then loaded until failure of the notched wires occurred and the resulting amplitude values recorded. The results were then used to produce a graph showing the variation in amplitude as the distance from the wire breaks to the transducer increased. Holford developed this work further and was successful in detecting outer wire breaks up to distances of 46 m using ropes ranging in diameter from 10-28 mm. Simple linear source location experiments were performed, using the Dunegan-Endevco system, with a high degree of success. Ropes with notches introduced into the other wires at known locations were loaded until these wires failed. The locations of the wire breaks provided by the acoustic emission equipment were in very close agreement with the actual positions.

The results of this work were used to design a simple wire break detector; however, a facility to locate wire breaks was not provided. This instrument was successful in detecting wire breaks in ropes subjected to both static or cyclic loading. Improvements to wire break detector designs were made as a result of analysing the transducer signals resulting from wire breaks in terms of amplitude, duration and frequency components. The work showed that the main frequency components of the transducer signals resulting from wire breaks were occupying the region up to 75 kHz with some high amplitude components having a frequency of the order of 10 kHz. This is in agreement with the signal analysis work carried out in (9); however, the work at Cardiff did not consider resonant frequencies of the rope specimen and test machine.

CORRELATION OF ACOUSTIC EMISSION ACTIVITY TO CHANGES IN WIRE ROPE PROPERTIES

In 1984 the Department of Energy sponsored a short test programme at the National Engineering Laboratory to investigate the scale effect and repeatability of the endurances of ropes of different diameter, when subjected to fluctuating tensile loads of constant amplitude. Three diameters of rope were used (40, 70 and 127 mm) and each one consisted of six multi-layer outer strands which surrounded a small six-strand independent wire rope core (IWRC). It was during this study that Casey and Waters (20,21) observed that changes in rope properties occurred during testing, including stiffness and elongation. It was also demonstrated that the resulting plots of stiffness and elongation against per cent life could be used to distinguish between ropes which achieved representative endurances and those which failed prematurely. Rope stiffness is defined as the gradient of the rising load portion of a fatigue load cycle and elongation is a measure of the permanent increase in rope length which takes place throughout a fatigue test. Rapid changes take place in the early stages of a test as the rope undergoes a bedding-in process where the strands and wires seat down on one another. As the test progresses further changes in the rope properties take place which result from, or are the effect of, significant numbers of wire breaks. Recent work by Casey (22) involved monitoring rope hysteresis which is the net work expended during a fatigue cycle and is the area enclosed by the loading and unloading curves. This work showed that changes in hysteresis correlated with the changes in stiffness but as stiffness decreased hysteresis increased and vice versa.

A secondary objective of the study was to evaluate available non-destructive testing techniques for assessing the condition of the large diameter wire ropes under test. When the test programme was being considered, research into the acoustic emission monitoring of small diameter ropes at Cardiff was advanced and these techniques were employed therefore to monitor some of the 40 mm diameter ropes being tested at NEL. This work was carried out with an improved wire break detector that incorporated some of the findings which resulted from analysing the transducer signals produced by wire breaks (16,18). The tests were carried out with the transducers attached to the end connections and poor correlations between recorded events and wire breaks were obtained (19). This is because in a tested 40 mm diameter rope specimen of length 3.8 m there was of the order of 6000 wire breaks, approximately 85 per cent of which were within the IWRC. The occurrence of such large numbers of wire breaks within the IWRC during a test will eventually hinder the propagation and hence the detection of the stress waves from resulting IWRC wire breaks. Clearly, the approach adopted which was so successful in monitoring the condition of small diameter ropes did not apply to large diameter ropes when subjected to tension-tension fatigue until failure.

The ropes which are now under investigation at NEL are being monitored with a commercially available acoustic emission system, an AVT Vulcan. A block diagram of the system as set up for wire rope monitoring is shown in Fig 1. This system assesses the incoming data and rejects, by the use of suitable transducer hit order sequences, spurious information originating from outside of the specimen being monitored. It also has the ability to reject data originating within the rope specimen but which is not regarded as relevant. It achieves this with an adjustable cluster threshold. The use of the cluster threshold means that a given number of acoustic emission bursts have to originate from a specific location within the rope in order to be accepted as relevant data. As with other acoustic emission systems, the Vulcan locates sources of acoustic emission by using the difference in the time of arrival at two or more transducers. The data recorded by the Vulcan is stored in bubble memory and this is then transferred to a microcomputer for subsequent post-processing and analysis. For the acoustic emission work now being carried out on large diameter wire rope, two transducers are attached to each end connection and the system is configured to detect large amounts of data during a fatigue test. For the present, rather than try to determine the exact mechanisms producing the acoustic emission, the data are correlated with changes in stiffness and hysteresis which take place throughout the test. The reason for doing this is to provide additional information which will deepen our understanding of the behaviour of large diameter wire ropes when subjected to tension-tension fatigue.

Presented in Fig 2 are the acoustic emission amplitude distributions resulting from a test carried out on a 70 mm diameter six-strand rope of length 3.6 m. Fig 2a shows the acoustic activity that occurred within the rope specimen including the emissions originating within the end connections, most of which can be attributed to the resin cappings. Examination shows that the amplitude distribution consists of three peaks, one between 40 and 60 dB, one between 60 and 80 dB and the third above 80 dB. For Fig 2b the emissions resulting from within the end connections have been filtered out and although the number of acoustic emission bursts is reduced, the shape of the distribution is unchanged. From this, it can be concluded that the activity generated within the end connections is continuous and not specific to one particular amplitude range.

The comparison between acoustic emission output and rope stiffness for this test is shown in Fig 3. Only the activity which originated from within the rope has been presented and it has been grouped into the three amplitude ranges, which can be referred to as low, medium and high activity respectively. The acoustic emission activity is presented in cumulative form, expressed as a percentage of the total number of acoustic emission bursts detected in each amplitude range and plotted against per cent life. Rope stiffness has also been expressed as a percentage and plotted against per cent life. As the rope bedded in and the stiffness increased, small amounts of low to medium amplitude acoustic emission activity occurred. It must be mentioned at this stage that the point in life where stiffness starts to decrease and hysteresis starts to increase, as a result of measurable rope degradation, is dependent upon load range. In general, the lower the test load the earlier in life where stiffness decreases and hysteresis starts to increase. These findings will be presented in detail in a future publication but the above statement should be taken into account when reading the remainder of this section. For this test the stiffness started to reduce at around 20 per cent life and at 16 per cent life there was a rapid increase in low amplitude acoustic emission activity. At 24 per cent life the high level activity started and then ceased at 26 per cent life. Increases in the high level activity again occurred at 47 and 88 per cent of life and examination of the stiffness plot shows that the rate of stiffness reduction increased at these points. Changes in the continuous low to medium activity occurred at 40 and 90 per cent of life. For this test it is believed that at around 20 per cent of life wire break activity was taking place within the IWRC. During the last 12 per cent of life, significant wire break activity was taking place in the multi-layer outer strands, in particular the outer wires. The activity which took place at mid life is also believed to be related to wire breaks but at present it cannot be stated with confidence whether the breaks are occurring in the independent wire rope core, the multi-layer outer strands or both.

The comparison between acoustic emission activity (again expressed in the three amplitude ranges) and rope properties represented in Fig 4 resulted from a fatigue test which was again carried out on a 70 mm diameter six-strand rope of length 3.6 m. Examination of the stiffness plot in Fig 4a shows a sudden fall-off at around 10 per cent of life and coinciding with this was low level acoustic emission activity. This sudden stiffness loss, which was not usual for the load range used, has been attributed to the viscosity of the rope blocking material reducing as the temperature increased. After the rope had bedded in the stiffness started to increase because the rope temperature decreased and the viscosity of the blocking material increased. After this initial activity, the acoustic emission output was very low until the region of 40 per cent life when a large amount of low to medium acoustic emission activity took place. The high amplitude acoustic emission activity was just beginning when the memory capacity of the Vulcan was exceeded and the data lost. For this test the stiffness started to reduce at 40 per cent of life. The Vulcan was reset at 60 per cent of life and large amounts of data were recorded as the stiffness reduced sharply. At 80 per cent life the memory capacity of the Vulcan was again exceeded but once reset at 95 per cent life much high amplitude activity was detected as the rope approached main failure. Figure 4b shows the acoustic emission activity compared with the hysteresis changes. Again, the acoustic emission activity is related to the hysteresis changes, the main difference being that the stiffness fluctuations in the early stages of the test are accompanied by only small changes in hysteresis. Figure 5 shows the correlation between acoustic emission, stiffness and hysteresis from the same test but this time the acoustic emission activity was not grouped into amplitude ranges. Instead, only the activity which occurred during the top 9 per cent of the fatigue load cycle has been presented, the assumption being that most of the wire break related activity would occur near to the top of the fatigue cycle. Examination of Fig 5 shows no acoustic emission activity was present in the early stages of the test where the stiffness suddenly reduced indicating that no wire break activity occurred. The acoustic emission activity started at 40 per cent of life exactly, at the point where the stiffness started to reduce and the hysteresis to increase. This represents the point in life at which detectable degradation of the rope started to take place. With the exception of where data was lost resulting from memory overflow, the acoustic emission activity continued until failure.

The correlation between rope properties and acoustic emission is not always so obvious. A 70 mm diameter rope was tested at the same load range as the test represented in Figs 4 and 5 but in this case premature failure of an outer strand at one of the terminations occurred. Examination of the stiffness plot in Fig 6 shows that after the bedding-in process the stiffness remained constant until 70 per cent of life when it started to reduce and failure of the strand at 90 per cent of life is shown clearly as a very large stiffness loss. Immediately after the strand failure, the stiffness increased slightly and then continued to reduce until the rope could no longer support the test load. For this example the acoustic activity occurring within the end connections has been included in the cumulative activity plot in Fig 6 The activity started at around 10 per cent of life and continued until failure. Most of the activity occurred between 40 and 65 per cent of life and the plateau in this region resulted from the memory capacity of the system being exceeded. At 70 per cent of life there was an increase in activity which corresponded to the commencement of stiffness fall-off but there was no significant activity prior to the failure of the strand. Also presented in Fig 6 is the activity of amplitude >80 dB which occurred during the last 19 per cent of the fatigue load cycle and the graph is very similar to that for the activity throughout the entire fatigue load cycle. Figure 7a shows the linear source location plot for all of the activity throughout this test and whilst a lot of activity originated from both end connections, there was significantly more activity from the end connection where failure occurred. The linear source location plot in Fig 7b represents the activity of amplitude >80 dB that occurred during the last 19 per cent of the fatigue load cycle. Whilst it shows that large amounts of activity originated from the end connection where failure occurred, no activity originated from the other end connection.

Within a wire rope specimen there are a number of possible sources of acoustic activity including interwire fretting, cracking of the capping resin, wire breaks and movement of broken wires during the fatigue cycle. It cannot be stated at this stage whether fatigue crack growth is being detected or not.

POSSIBLE PRACTICAL APPLICATIONS OF ACOUSTIC
EMISSION MONITORING OF WIRE ROPE

Of the degradation processes which can occur within a wire rope acoustic emission is possibly best suited to detect wire breaks; however, because a wire break is an irreversible event, the rope has to be monitored continuously. Also as illustrated in this paper, if very large amounts of wire breaks take place then the detection rate will decrease. With these factors in mind, based on the work conducted to date, suggestions will now be put forward for the possible use of acoustic emission in applications outside the laboratory. For most applications it would be impractical, if not impossible, to monitor a wire rope continuously over its entire length. Therefore, for a given situation it is important that specific areas of weakness be identified so that they can be monitored. One of these areas of weakness is where a rope passes around a pulley and Torangi and Taylor (23) obtained very good correlations between recorded events and wire breaks when monitoring bending over sheave tests at the British Ropes Laboratory in Doncaster; 12 mm diameter six-strand rope was used with transducers located on the pulleys. A possible future application of this type of monitoring could be at the fairlead pulleys of a floating production platform. At this area the mooring ropes are subjected to a fatigue loading condition known as bending-tension fatigue. This type of loading involves small movements of the rope about the pulley in phase with fluctuating tensile loads and is due to wind, tide and wave effects.

Localised damage can occur at the rope where it moves on and off the pulley and this area of the rope could possibly be monitored with transducers located somewhere on the pulley system. Two main problems would have to be overcome, namely the protection of the transducers and preamplifiers from the environment and the filtering out of extraneous noise sources. The main processing equipment could be housed within the platform and in addition to detecting individual wire breaks the system could also be set up to monitor changes in overall acoustic activity.

Strands used for bridge hangers is another potential application for acoustic emission monitoring. Unlike the six-strand wire ropes under investigation at NEL a spiral strand does not have the complication of an independent wire rope core. As a result signal attenuation from wire breaks would be expected to be less of a problem and this has been confirmed in a test carried out at NEL on a 7 m length of large diameter strand, with the transducer mounted on one of the end connections, which yielded a very good correlation between recorded events and wire breaks. Possibly all that would be required to monitor a strand would be a transducer tuned to the main frequency components of a wire break, a suitably filtered amplifier, a detection threshold, an event timer and a suitable hard copy counter. The unit could be produced in the form of a small black box and strapped to one of the end connections. Equipment of this type could also be used to monitor both rope and strand for wire breaks occurring in the neck of the sockets.

Matthews and Black (24) carried out an investigation into the acoustic emission signature of wire breaks in the cables used to tow sonar depth testing bodies. This work resulted in the design of a monitoring system and was later improved by Matthews and others (25). The transducer was taped to the termination with its face towards the axis of the rope, water being used as the coupling medium. Work presented in (18) showed that it is possible to detect wire breaks with a transducer located 100 mm away from the rope with water as the coupling medium. The face of the transducer was in contact with the water and perpendicular to the axis of the rope. If work of this nature is continued one could speculate that the sections of mooring ropes which are positioned on the seabed could be monitored with suitable sensors positioned near to the rope and anchored to the seabed. Major difficulties would have to be overcome, however, not least being the design and location of the processing equipment.

Of the ideas put forward, the monitoring of bridge hangers near to the terminations is possibly the one application that could be attempted immediately. In fact, it is thought that the authors in (8) have carried out tests on bridge hangers at various sites throughout France.

CONCLUSIONS

Correlations have been shown to exist between acoustic emission activity and changes in mechanical properties when wire ropes are subjected to constant amplitude tension-tension fatigue. The work has helped to identify specific stages in a fatigue test where large amounts of wire break activity take place and provides valuable information concerning how a large diameter wire rope deteriorates under tension-tension fatigue. The sources of acoustic emission activity within a wire rope specimen include wire breaks, interwire fretting and emissions from the end connections, in particular the resin cappings. It cannot be concluded at this stage that fatigue crack growth is being detected.

ACKNOWLEDGEMENTS

The author acknowledges with gratitude the assistance provided by Mr R Belshaw and Dr J Fairbairn, Manager of the Structural Testing and Analysis Division, NEL.

REFERENCES

(1)   Savill, LP, Parameters which Affect the Endurance of Wire Ropes - A Ropemaker's Viewpoint, Wire Industry, Vol 47, No 554, Feb 1980, pp 375-381.

(2)   National Coalboard, Ropeman's Handbook, 3rd Edition, Published by Clarke Constable Ltd, 1980.

(3)   Egan, RA, Non-destructive Testing of Wire Ropes, 9th Annual Offshore Technology Conference, Houston, Texas, OTC 2926, 2-5 May 1977, pp 375-381.

(4)   Babel, H, Destructive and Non-destructive Testing Methods to Determine the Life of Wire Rope - 2, Wire, Vol 30, No 1, Jan-Feb 1980, pp 38-44.

(5)   Laura, PA and others, Acoustic Detection of Structural Failure of Mechanical Cables, The Journal of the Acoustical Society of America, Vol 45, No 3, 1969, pp 791-793.

(6)   Laura, PA and others, Mechanical Behaviour of Stranded Wire Rope and Feasibility of Detection of Cable Failure, Marine Technology Society Journal, Vol 4, No 3, May-June 1970, pp 19-32.

(7)   Harris, DO and Dunegan, HL, Acoustic Emission Testing of Wire Rope, Materials Evaluation, Vol 32, No 1, Jan 1974, pp 1-6.

(8)   Bamberger, Y and Robert, JL, Acoustic Testing of Cables, 1st European Conference on Non-destructive Testing, Mainz, Germany, Vol 2 (Proc Conf), 24-26 April 1978, pp 355-360.

(9)   Fritz, JTD and others, Experimental Development of a Wire Rope Monitoring Device for Laboratory Fatigue Testing, CSIR Contract Report ME 1593, Pretoria, South Africa, Sept 1978.

(10)   Hanzawa, M and others, Fatigue Behaviour of Large Diameter Wire Ropes, Society of Petroleum Engineers Journal, Vol 23, No 3, June 1982, pp 420-428.

(11)   Casey, NF, The Evaluation of Wire Ropes by Acoustic Emission and Other Techniques, PhD Thesis, 1984.

(12)   Holford, KM, Non-destructive testing of Wire Ropes by Acoustic Emission, PhD Thesis, 1987.

(13)   Taylor, JL and Casey, NF, The Acoustic Emission of Steel Wire Ropes, Wire Industry, Vol 51, No 601, Jan 1984, pp 79-82.

(14)   Casey, NF and others, The Acoustic Detection of the Failure of Constituent Wires of Wire Rope, Wire Industry, Vol 52, No 617, May 1985, pp 307-309.

(15)   Casey, NF and Taylor, JL, The Evaluation of Wire Ropes by Acoustic Emission Techniques, British Journal of Non-destructive Testing, Nov 1985, pp 351-356.

(16)   Casey, NF and others, Frequency Analysis of the Signals Generated by the Failure of Constituent Wires of Wire Rope, NDT International, Vol 18, No 6, Dec 1985, pp 339-344.

(17)   Casey, NF and Taylor, JL, An Instrument for the Evaluation of Wire Ropes: A Progress Report. British Journal of Non-destructive Testing, Jan 1987, pp 18-21.

(18)   Casey, NF and others, The Acoustic Evaluation of Wire Ropes Immersed in
         Water. NDT International Vol 20, No 3, June 1987, pp 173-176.

(19)   Casey, NF and others, Wire Break Detection During the Tensile Fatigue Testing
         of 40 mm diameter Wire Rope, The British Journal of Non-destructive Testing,
         Vol 30, No 5, Sept 1988, pp 338-341.

(20)   Casey, NF and Waters, DM, Observations on the Stiffness and Elongation of
         Large Diameter Wire Rope during Tensile Fatigue Testing, Wire Industry,
         Vol 54, No 641, May 1987, pp 300-303.

(21)   Casey, NF and Waters, DM, Presentation of the Findings of a Test Programme
         Conducted to Determine the Fatigue Behaviour of Large Diameter Wire Ropes,
         Wire Industry, Vol 55, No 653, May 1988, pp 371-378.

(22)   Casey, NF, Monitoring Wire Rope Properties during Tension-Tension Fatigue
         Testing, Wire Industry, Vol 55, No 659, Nov 1988, pp 758-761.

(23)   Torangi Sarjamee, SZ and Taylor, JL, Aspects of Acoustic Emission of Wire
         Ropes - Final Report, SERC/MTD Managed Programme on the Behaviour of
         Wire Ropes in Offshore Applications, June 1987.

(24)   Matthews, JR and Black, MR, Acoustic Emission Signature of Variable Depth
         Sonar Tow Cable, International Advances in Non-destructive Testing, Vol 7,
         1981, pp 181-214.

(25)   Matthews, JR and others, Cable Integrity by Acoustic Emission, US Patent
         No 4,565,964, Jan 1986.

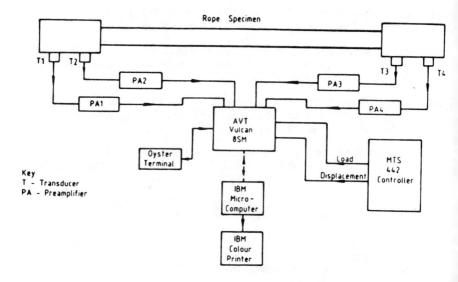

Fig 1 Block diagram of the experimental set-up

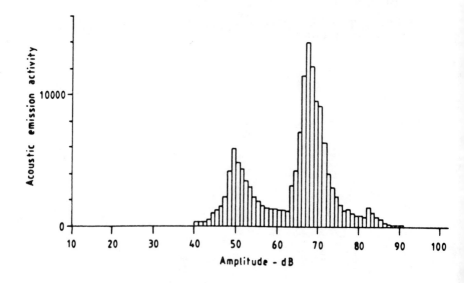

Fig 2a Amplitude distribution; including end connection activity

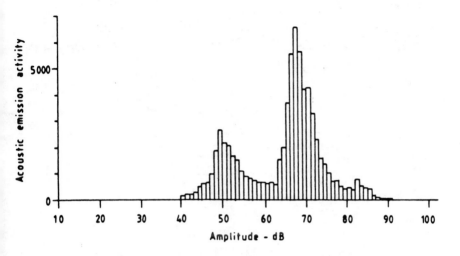

Fig 2b Amplitude distribution; end connection activity removed

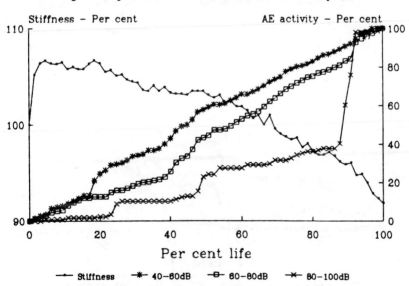

Fig 3 Correlation between acoustic emission activity and stiffness

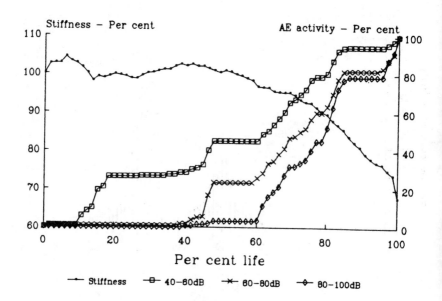

Fig 4a Correlation between acoustic emission activity and stiffness

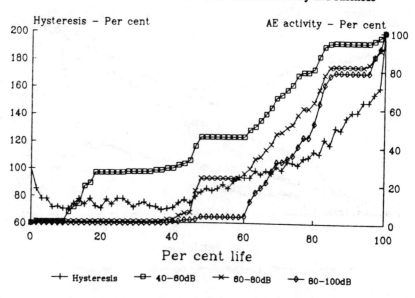

Fig 4b Correlation between acoustic emission activity and hysteresis

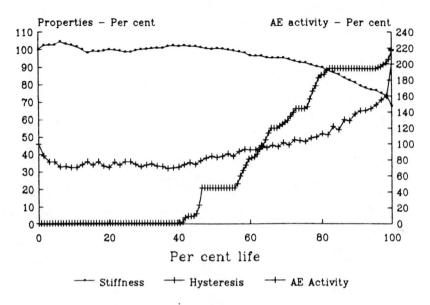

Fig 5 Correlation between acoustic emission activity, stiffness and hysteresis. Activity during the top 9 per cent of cycle

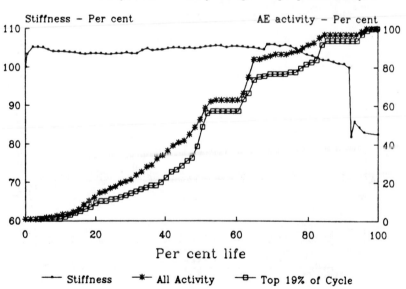

Fig 6 Comparison between acoustic emission activity and stiffness, premature failure

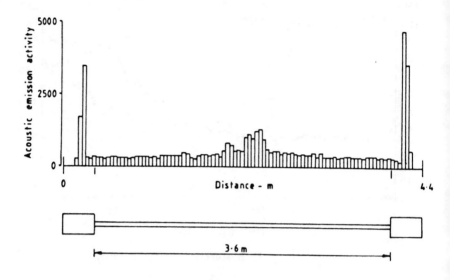

Fig 7a   Linear source location plot; all activity

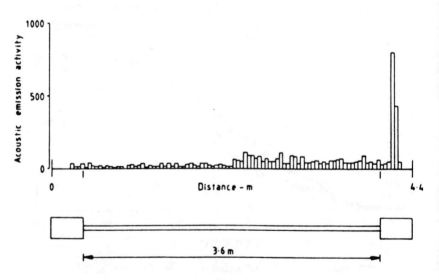

Fig 7b   Linear source location plot: Activity >80 dB
and during last 19 per cent of cycle

FIELD EXPERIENCE IN THE NON DESTRUCTIVE TESTING OF
WIRE ROPES

NIGEL TURNER

This paper outlines some of the practical aspects
which need to be taken into account when using non
destructive testing to assess wire rope condition.

The information presented is based upon experience
gained over some twelve years in the examination of
wire ropes on mine hoists, underground haulages,
cable cars, chair lifts, blondins/cable cranes,
lifts/elevators and a number of other types of
installation.

A wide variety of wire ropes types and constructions
has been involved and examinations have been made in a
number of countries other than in the United Kingdom.

Introduction

In this paper two levels of wire rope condition assessment are
referred to. They are an inspection and an examination. We define
the difference as follows.

An inspection is a careful and critical visual assessment of a wire
rope carried out by an inspector, who in many cases will be a
person employed in a mechanical engineering maintenance department
and being a person not full time professionally engaged in wire
rope condition assessment.

An examination is a careful and critical assessment of a wire rope
carried out by a wire rope examiner who, in all cases, will be a
person professionally engaged in wire rope condition assessment.
An examination would include, where necessary and possible, non
destructive testing, supplemented when required by a visual
assessment of the internal condition of the wire rope.

Rope Technical Site Services Ltd., 5 St. George's Road, Bessacarr,
Doncaster, South Yorkshire. DN4 5LP

Wire ropes deteriorate both externally and internally. All deterioration reduces the ability of a wire rope to withstand the forces applied to it and, if the rope is not withdrawn from service in time, will ultimately fail.

Within the United Kingdom, with the exception of a few wire rope users, visual inspection is the only form of wire rope condition assessment carried out.

On long lengths of wire rope or heavily lubricated wire rope, visual condition assessment is extremely difficult, particularly so where inspections or examinations have to be carried out under adverse conditions. It is also an alarming fact that even external deterioration is not being detected or recognised at visual inspections and/or wire ropes are deteriorating internally whilst external inspection has passed them fit to remain in service.

Visual assessment of wire rope condition also fails in that there is no permanent record to be filed for future reference. A change in personnel, differences in written descriptions and a variance in the opinions of individuals all contribute to an inconsistency of decision making and reporting of wire rope condition.

Visual inspection or visual examination is therefore not a totally satisfactory method for assessing wire rope condition and in some cases wire ropes are prematurely removed from service to take account of this fact, or remain in service long after the time when they should have been discarded.

The Alternative to Visual Wire Rope Condition Assessment

The most effective form of wire rope condition assessment is an examination completed with the aid of one of the wide variety of N.D.T. instruments specifically designed for this purpose.

These instruments allow an effective examination to be made of a wire rope over its full accessible length, regardless of the amount of lubricant present, both externally and internally.

Most modern instruments will detect faults/deterioration which take the form of broken wires, corrosion, interwire/interstrand marking and localised abrasion, and some instruments will detect general loss in metallic cross sectional area.

Indeed, in many countries this technique is considered so reliable that regular non destructive testing is mandatory.

Practical Application of Non Destructive Testing

The full benefit of non destructive testing can only be achieved if
a picture is built up of the changes which occur in a wire rope
throughout its service life and a comparison is made of results
currently obtained with those from preceding examinations.

The interval between examinations very much depends upon the rate of
rope deterioration and will vary from one installation to another.

Since non destructive testing is an aid to wire rope condition
assessment, no examination is complete without a visual examination
being made of at least some of the sections of wire rope which the
instrument indicates as containing deterioration/faults.

An ideal situation is where an examination can be made within a few
weeks of the installation of a new rope. The trace thus obtained
can be used as a datum or reference trace. By completing regular
examinations, deterioration can be detected and identified at a time
relatively close to its development. At subsequent examinations,
only those lengths/positions which exhibit increased deterioration
may need to be examined in detail.

In addition to recording and assessing deterioration/faults which
can be detected by the N.D.T. instrument there are many other forms
of deterioration/faults and changes in wire rope condition which
need to be considered if a complete assessment of wire rope
condition is to be made.

By reference to the following list of items which need to be
considered by a rope examiner, it can easily be seen that the
information provided by an N.D.T. instrument is only a part of the
information required.

It is not sufficient only to pass the rope through the detecting
head.

It follows that rope inspections may be satisfactory for the
regular weekly/monthly assessment of rope condition but that
professional examination is periodically required. Also that
examinations should be entrusted only to those companies/
organisations which can show that they are specialists in the
subject of wire ropes and not to organisations which, because they
have purchased an N.D.T. instrument, consider themselves competent
wire rope examiners.

Further, although it may appear very simple to use an N.D.T.
instrument, and in fact obtaining traces is not very difficult,
obtaining meaningful traces, interpreting the results and

understanding an instrument so that it is used to its best advantage requires a considerable amount of experience.

The forms of deterioration which need to be considered when determining wire rope condition are as follows.

1. Number and nature of broken wires (both visible external broken wires and internal broken wires).
2. Wire breaks at the termination/deterioration of the termination.
3. Local groups of broken wires (broken wires concentrated in 1 or 2 strands).
4. The rate of increase of wire breaks.
5. Broken strands.
6. Reduction or increase in rope diameter.
7. External wear.
8. Internal wear.
9. Core deterioration.
10. Decreased elasticity.
11. Rate of increase of permanent elongation.
12. External corrosion.
13. Internal corrosion.
14. Abnormal damage and deformations.
15. Thermal damage - damage due to heat or electric arc-ing.

Objects at Each Examination

In principle the objects at each full examination of a wire rope should be:

1. To obtain a trace for as much of the rope length as possible.
2. To analyse the trace with regard to both external and internal deterioration/faults and where necessary physically locate deterioration/faults in order to confirm the analysis of the trace.
3. To determine the maximum incidence of broken wires within the relevant reference length.
4. To note the degree of change which has taken place in respect of all the other forms of deterioration referred to in the list above.
5. To assess the condition of the lubricant.
6. To obtain a set of rope diameter measurements representative of the rope as a whole and to determine the percentage reduction which has taken place from the nominal rope diameter.
7. To examine visually all those sections of rope which it is not possible to pass through the detecting head.
8. To consider all the findings of the examination and report on the rope condition.

Presentation of Results and Findings

Because, as was said earlier, the full benefit of an N.D.T. examination can only be achieved if a picture is built up of the changes which occur in a wire rope throughout its life, reports need therefore to be presented in such a manner as to allow all aspects of deterioration to be recorded throughout the life of the wire rope and for a comparison of the results to be readily undertaken.

A typical full report for a wire rope which it would be expected would remain in service for a period of years rather than months, would include the following sections.

1. Introduction.
2. Installation and rope details.
3. Findings and comments/conclusions/recommendations, i.e. the findings at each examination, together with relevant comments and conclusions regarding the fitness of the rope to continue in service and appropriate recommendations. In this section would be given details of any lengths of the wire rope which were either only visually examined or not examined at all.
4. Examination procedure.
5. Various data sheets, but including a data sheet tabulating the findings from the visual examinations made within the rope length and a data sheet giving the rejection factor for the rope as a whole and/or at specific positions of deterioration.
6. Assessment of rejection factors. In order to assess when a wire rope should be withdrawn from service, some scheme for quantifying and adding the effect of different forms of deterioration needs to be employed. A section would be included detailing the forms of deterioration to be considered and the scheme used to quantify and add the different forms of deterioration, in order to calculate a rejection factor. This section would also detail the regulations or code of practice governing the use of the wire rope in question.

Which Ropes can be Examined?

Wire ropes on most installations can be examined, although this form of examination is best suited to long lengths of wire rope which are difficult to examine visually and which have a high capital replacement value, or which are used on installations subject to rigorous safety regulations.

Examples are:

Mine hoisting ropes and guide ropes
Cable crane (blondin) track, hauling and hoisting ropes

Cable car/aerial ropeway track and hauling ropes
Ski/chair lift ropes
Passenger/goods lift ropes in high rise buildings

With regard to diameter limitations, our own capability currently
covers the range 8 (mm) to 85 (mm) inclusive. Most wire rope types
and constructions can be satisfactorily examined.

Practical Considerations before commencing an Examination

Before commencing an examination the following items need to be
considered. This is not an exhaustive list and the items detailed
refer only to the use of the N.D.T. equipment and not to the
necessary considerations in respect of rope examination techniques.

1. Where and in how many positions does the detecting head require
   to be positioned so that the maximum length of wire rope
   possible can be passed through the detector? On some installations it is not possible to position the detecting head at all
   of the positions required and therefore in some instances a
   compromise is necessary. However, it should never be the case
   that a length of wire rope is not passed through the detecting
   head in which the examiner believes that there is the possibility of significant deterioration, unless that deterioration can
   be detected by other means.
2. Are there any items of plant or machinery in close proximity to
   the chart recorder which could result in extraneous signals
   being recorded or excessive vibrations in the wire rope under
   examination in the region of the detecting head, which could
   influence the results being recorded?
3. How safe are the locations at which the N.D.T. equipment is to
   be positioned in respect of the personnel working with the
   equipment, the installation and the equipment itself?
4. How effective is the communication with the operator/driver of
   the appliance? The ability to stop the wire rope or the
   appliance instantaneously is essential for safe working.
5. How is the detecting head to be positioned and held in place
   around the wire rope?
6. Can the wire rope be accessed at or close to the same position
   as the detecting head for the purpose of visually examining
   positions at which faults or deterioration occur?
7. At what speed/s can the wire rope be passed through the
   detecting head or the detecting head over the wire rope? How
   variable and controllable is the speed? Can the direction of
   travel be reversed? How fast can the wire rope be stopped?
8. Ensure that the appliance operator/driver and other relevant
   personnel understand what is required of them during the
   conducting of the examination.

Having considered all of the items detailed in 1 to 8 above, the instrument settings can be determined. These will vary depending upon the type of installation, the rope speed and the type, diameter and construction of the wire rope.

Examination Procedure

Having determined the required and best position/s for the detecting head and positioned this about the wire rope, the wire rope is passed through the detecting head at the required speed.

A visual record of the condition of the rope is produced on to a paper trace, in the form of a graph, by the chart recorder.

Traces are obtained at various sensitivity settings and chart speeds to allow different features of any faults/deteriorations to be highlighted and analysed.

Where necessary a visual examination is made at any positions in the wire rope which the traces indicate as containing specific faults/deterioration. This is in order to confirm the analysis of the trace and to determine the exact details of any fault or deterioration.

In some instances visual internal examinations are carried out.

Where possible a visual examination is made of those lengths of the wire rope which cannot be passed through the detecting head, and of the end terminations. If the wire rope contains any long splices, these are always visually examined.

Diameter measurements are taken at regular intervals throughout the wire rope length so as to be representative of the wire rope as a whole and at any positions of specific faults/deterioration. At these same positions a visual assessment of the wire rope condition is made in respect of those features of change or deterioration which cannot be detected by the N.D.T. instrument.

How much Time is Required to Complete an N.D.T. Examination?

The time required to complete an examination depends principally on the type of installation, the accessibility of the wire rope and the condition of the wire rope at the time of the examination.

The time required cannot be directly related to the wire rope length.

It must not be assumed that an N.D.T. examination is automatically a faster solution to wire rope condition assessment than any system currently being employed by a wire rope user. This is because an N.D.T. examination will generally detect all the faults/deterioration which are present in a wire rope, many of which would perhaps not normally be detected, and because a professional examination with the aid of N.D.T. techniques would, we expect, be far more thorough than the normal wire rope inspections which are carried out.

Difficulties which can be Experienced in the Execution of an N.D.T. Examination and in the Determination of Wire Rope Condition

A number of factors, which can occur either individually or in combination, makes the task of wire rope examination, by N.D.T. methods and wire rope condition assessment, more difficult than it may at first seem.

The following list is not exhaustive, but is sufficient to show that wire rope condition assessment, even when aided by the obvious advantages of using N.D.T. techniques, is not something which can be entrusted lightly to persons with little knowledge of wire ropes or wire rope examination techniques.

1. Practical difficulties which can influence the extent to which a wire rope is, or can be, examined, include:
   (a) general access to the wire rope/s
   (b) the danger element in going to where it is necessary to make the examination
   (c) communication with the appliance operator
   (d) lighting and weather conditions
   (e) wire rope fittings or adjacent steelwork interfering with access to sections of the wire rope
2. Technical factors or considerations which need to be taken into account include:
   (a) the fact that any traces being recorded can be affected by
       (i) wide variations in the speed at which the wire rope is passing through the detecting head
       (ii) excessive vibration in the wire rope
       (iii) the close proximity of some types of electrical equipment
   (b) that it is essential to select the correct or most appropriate sensitivity setting and chart paper speed for the diameter, type and construction of wire rope being examined
   (c) understanding that
       (i) the same type of deterioration can result in a different trace pattern depending upon the wire rope construction
       (ii) that the same number of broken wires occurring at different positions in the same wire rope can produce a different trace pattern

(iii)   significant deterioration may be present in a wire
        rope even though first analysis of the trace
        indicates little deterioration
(d) that it is necessary to be able to interpret any traces
     obtained based upon the knowledge of
     (i)   the types of deterioration one would expect to find
           in a particular type of wire rope or which normally
           occur on a particular type of installation
     (ii) any extraordinary factors relating to the specific
           installation in question
     (iii) the past history of the wire rope under examination
           and of preceding wire ropes
(e) generally understanding wire rope behaviour
3. The time available to make the examination
4. Application of regulations. In many cases wire ropes have to be
    examined for which there are no specific discard criteria laid
    down, or for which the regulations are not very clear or
    specific.

Based upon experience it is necessary to examine the wire rope in
question in as much depth as possible in the time available and
under the conditions prevailing, to the extent that one is satisfied
beyond reasonable doubt that the areas of greatest deterioration
have been assessed, but making sure that any report states which
sections of the wire rope it was not possible to examine, and that
the client is fully aware of all these factors.

If any doubt exists as to the fitness of the wire rope to continue
in service, the rope should be changed unless further examination
can dispel these doubts.

It follows from the above that potential users of a non destructive
testing service or any service related to the examination of wire
ropes should be most careful where they obtain that service.

The Cost Effectiveness of Contracting Professional Examinations Using N.D.T. Techniques

It is obvious that there is little point in contracting this type of
service if the cost of the examinations would be greater than a
straightforward rope replacement programme, on the same time scale
as these examinations would require.

This form of wire rope examination is generally most useful to users
of wire ropes:

(a) with a high capital replacement value
(b) which are subject to rigorous safety regulations
(c) which are expensive to replace in terms of excessive machine
     downtime and labour involvement.

It is difficult to draw general conclusions when considering cost effectiveness and each case should be considered on its merits. It is true to say that in many cases, where the above facts are important considerations, ensuring wire ropes are not removed from service prematurely can effect savings.

There are also instances where to examine a single rope would not be at all cost effective, but by spreading the cost over a number of units which can all be examined on one service visit, this form of examination becomes a sensible option.

Justification for Professional Examination using N.D.T. Techniques based on Case Histories

The following are a few examples of wire ropes which Ropetech has been called upon to examine.

In those cases where the rope was found to be in a discard condition the client in every case, as far as we know, was totally unaware that the ropes in question had reached an advanced state of deterioration.

1. Cable Crane Track Ropes - examined July 1984
    2 x 520 (m), 61 (mm) diameter full locked coil. Both ropes previously in service for 30 months followed by storage, 1 rope for 11 years, 1 rope for 15 years, condition of ropes unknown. Both ropes examined and passed fit for service. Ropes subsequently installed and went on to give 2½ years further service. Saving to client in excess of £10,000.

2. Mine Hoist Ropes - Koepe (friction) winder - examined March 1986
    4 x 29 (mm) diameter, 6x22 triangular strand, fibre core, langs lay, galvanised. At first examination after 2 years' service:
    no significant number of broken wires in any rope
    maximum reductions in diameter from nominal over the 4 ropes 10.52% to 11.69%
    moderate to heavy wear on the strand crowns, heavy in places
    moderate to heavy surface corrosion in the strand gussets
    significant interstrand/interwire marking and internal corrosion
    subsequent workshop examinations and tests following removal from service showed a loss in aggregate breaking strength in the order of 20%

3. Cable Crane Hoist Rope - examined July 1986
    33 (mm) diameter, 6x31(12/6 and 6/6/1) fibre core, right hand ordinary lay. At second examination after 1 year 5 months' service:
    broken wires, 19 adjacent in the same strand made up of 9 broken outer wires and 10 broken inner wires, 2 broken outer wires in the adjacent strand

reduction in diameter from nominal at same position 6.18%
Considered number of allowable broken outer wires:
I.S.O.4309 - 14 in 6 diameters when distributed between the
strands
Ropetech - as above but reduced to 7 in 6 diameters if
concentrated in 1 or 2 strands.

4. Cable Car Hauling Rope - height difference between stations 535
(m) - maximum gradient 200% - examined July 1986
29 (mm) diameter, 6x19(9/9/1) fibre core, langs lay. At first
examination after 9 years' service:
at numerous positions severe corrosion pitting, with some wires
almost corroded through
at 1 specific position 3 broken outer wires in 6 rope diameters
with 8 other outer wires so seriously affected by corrosion that
they could be considered as broken, equivalent to a total
reduction in section of 14% based on the steel cross sectional
area of the rope
at a further specific position extending over 19 strands, all of
the outer wires so seriously affected by corrosion that 50% of
them considered as contributing no strength to the rope,
equivalent to a reduction in section based on the steel cross
sectional area of the rope of more than 36%
Allowable reduction in section:
based on the steel cross sectional area of the rope, 6% in 6
diameters for localised severe wear or deterioration
based on the steel cross sectional area of the rope, 25% in 500
diameters for deterioration, which has resulted from normal
conditions of use and service.

5. Mine Hoist Ropes - Koepe (friction) winder - regularly examined
since November 1986
4 x 33 (mm) diameter, 6x19(6 and 6/6/1) fibre core, langs lay
Ropes first examined towards end of 2 year statutory life after
1 year 11 months' service. Examinations permitted extension.
Ropes to be changed January 1989 after 4 years' service. Saving
to client, in excess of £7,000.

6. Cable Crane Hauling Rope - examined August 1987
25 (mm) diameter, 6x36(14/7 and 7/7/1) fibre core, right hand
ordinary lay. At first examination:
broken outer wires, minimum of 8, maximum of 21, distributed
between the strands in 1 lay length
broken outer wires concentrated in 1 strand in 1 lay length,
values recorded of 5, 6, 7, 9
reduction in diameter from nominal in areas of broken wires,
maximum 4.8%
Considered number of allowable broken outer wires:
14 in 1 lay length if distributed between the strands, 7 in 1
lay length if concentrated in 1 or 2 strands

7. Mine Hoist Ropes - Drum Winder - examined October 1988
   1" diameter, 6x8 triangular strand, fibre core, right hand langs
   lay. At first examination after 13 years 8 months' service:
   cage hoist rope, in first 57 (m) above cage:
   moderate to heavy abrasive wear plus corrosion pitting along
   wire crowns
   significant corrosion pitting in strand gussets and wire
   interstices
   advanced internal corrosion
   no external broken wires and reduction in diameter from nominal
   of less than 1%
   counterweight hoist rope, in 51 (m) length commencing 44 (m)
   above counterweight:
   severe abrasive wear with outer wires reduced in diameter by up
   to 50% plus corrosion pitting along wire crowns
   significant internal corrosion
   significant numbers of internal broken wires.

NDT OF SEMI-SUBMERSIBLE PRODUCTION PLATFORM MOORINGS

T.G. BAVINS

The BP operated semi-submersible production platform Buchan Alpha is held on station using using a ten line catenary mooring system. To help maximise the service life of the moorings, BP has developed with Mera-Ster of Poland, a non-destructive test instrument to inspect the condition of the moorings in–situ.

The instrument has been extensively tested offshore and its use has been specified in the platform Operations Manual as part of the annual inspection requirement. The results from these inspections are used as part of the information required to satisfy Lloyd's Register of Shipping as to the condition and predicted lifetime of the moorings.

This paper outlines the system used, describes the inspection procedure, gives examples of typical inspection results and describes potential further developments of the system.

INTRODUCTION

On behalf of a joint venture consortium, BP operates a floating production platform called Buchan Alpha, in the Buchan field. This field is located 83 miles east-north-east of Aberdeen in a water depth of 120 metres. The Buchan Alpha platform is a pentagon shaped semi-submersible structure with catenary moorings. The mooring system consists of ten 71 mm diameter six strand ropes, each some 3400 metres long. To assess the condition and safety of the steel wire mooring lines, especially in damage–prone areas, BP has developed magnetic non-destructive testing equipment in conjunction with a Polish company (Mera-Ster), who manufacture devices for inspecting mining and crane ropes.

The NDT system developed enables BP to inspect the mooring lines for wire breaks, corrosion, abrasion and other damage. Inspections can be performed on moorings in–situ or after recovery.

BP Research International Ltd., Sunbury Research Centre,
Chertsey Road, Sunbury-on-Thames, Middlesex, TW16 7LN, UK.

The successful development and testing of the equipment has resulted in its inclusion in the platform's Operations Manual as a specific part of the annual platform inspection programme. The NDT results are combined with destructive testing results to provide an objective basis for assessing the condition of the moorings and projecting their remaining lifetime. This assessment is required by Lloyd's Register of Shipping, which governs the operation of rigs such as Buchan Alpha.

The regular use of this inspection system has significant cost saving and safety implications for the operators of the platform.

PROTOTYPE NDT SYSTEM

Background

A device or method was required that would enable accurate (in-situ) assessment of the condition of the mooring lines. In 1983/84 BP began a collaboration with Mera-Ster of Katowice, poland, to develop a marinised, large diameter wire rope inspection system. The system was based on an existing Mera-Ster device used to inspect large diameter mine and crane ropes, which was adapted and marinised for deployment in shallow water depths (up to 150 m).

This development was undertaken with funding from BP's Exploraration Group and in consultation with Engineering and Technical Support, BP Petroleum Development and Buchan Operations Group in Dyce.

Physical Principles

The principle of operation of the device is based on the ability of a wire rope to contain a magnetic field. Powerful permanent magnets magnetically saturate a rope section enclosed in the head.

The presence of small, localised defects within the rope cross-section will cause local distortions in the magnetic flux passing through the wires, resulting in flux leakage outside the rope, which are detected by sensor coils in the head.

Larger scale defects, such as abrasion, reduce the magnetic flux passing through the rope's cross-section. Under saturation conditions, the magnetic flux passing through the rope is directly related to its metallic cross-sectional area.

These defects can be located and characterised by combining magnetic saturation of the wire rope with a system for detection of flux leakage or changes in the magnetic field in the wire.

The Mera-Ster device employs the following two methods for defect detection:

(i)   Inductive Coil Sensors

These respond to localised defects as the wire is passed through the sensors. The inductance of the coils changes as each passes over the defect and the associated leakage flux. The output signal from the coils depends on the size of the defect and the speed of the rope through the coils.

(ii)   Hall Sensor Array

These sensors respond to more uniformly distributed wear and corrosion. The Hall sensors are mounted perpendicularly to the axis of the wire rope under the poles of the permanent magnets and operate independent of rope speed. They simply measure the strength of the magnetic field passing through the rope, which is directly related to its metallic cross-sectional area.

System Components

The developed prototype NDT system employs a combination of Hall sensors and coils so that all rope rope defects can be detected and assessed qualitatively and quantitatively.

The NDT equipment consists of the following items (Fig 1):

(i)   NDT Inspection Head

The inspection head is hinged and splits in half to allow attachment to the mooring rope. The head contains an arrangement of permanent magnets to magnetically saturate the rope section as it passes through. It also houses the search coils and the Hall sensor arrays. Some signal conditioning is carried out on board to amplify the voltage signals from the sensors and to adapt them to a 4-20 mA current loop communications system.

(ii)   Winch Cable

The head is lowered down the mooring line on a steel winch cable from a pneumatic winch and is then pulled back up at a constant speed during the inspection (typically 0.5 m/s).

(iii)   Power/Signal Cable

The electrical connection from the head to the topside instrumentation and the power supply is via 100 m of electrical umbilical cable containing power and signal cores.

(iv) Data Aquisition/Analysis Instrumentation

Topside instrumentation comprises an analogue tape recorder, digital data storage device, chart recorder, rope damage monitor and rope defect monitor. The data recorders allow subsequent reprocessing of the input signals if required. The rope damage monitor provides signal conditioning and chart trace outputs for each sensor array. The defect monitor records wire breaks and other anomalies within a specified length of rope and can indicate when discard criteria are reached.

WIRE ROPE INSPECTIONS

The NDT wire rope inspection equipment has been successfully employed for in-situ inspections of Buchan's moorings and for inspection of recovered lines and sections of those lines.

Buchan Moorings

Each Buchan mooring line extends vertically downwards from a winch to a fairlead pulley about 30 m below. About 600 m of mooring line stretches out from the fairlead to the seabed in a catenary shape. Approximately 1100 m from this 'touchdown' region is a connection to 1700 m of ground line which stretches away to an anchor (Fig. 2).

The winches are used to control the line tension so that the position of the platform above the template can be maintained or adjusted to accommodate production requirements or adverse weather conditions. Although Buchan Alpha is moored on station and does not winch/handle its mooring ropes as much as a mobile unit, there is still a possibility of damage to the moorings in the fairlead region where they pass over the fairlead pulley or are reeled on and off the winch drum.

A typical inspection exercise involves in-situ examination of the fairlead region of each mooring.

System Preparation

Prior to positioning on the mooring, the system is calibrated on a section of rope containing known defects (see section on Calibration). This enables quantitative assessment of any defects found during the inspection.

Because of the electrical power requirements of the equipment, 'hot work' permits must be obtained before an inspection can begin. The topside equipment is usually sited inside the platform leg adjacent to the mooring to protect it (and the operator) from the elements. The pneumatic winch is craned into position.

Fairlead Inspection

In order to inspect the fairlead section of the mooring, the line tension is increased by approximately ten tonnes - sufficient to reposition the length passing around the pulley so that it is above the fairlead. The head is then attached to the mooring line and lowered down to a point immediately above the fairlead - any marine growth or fouling on the rope is removed either by surface divers or by using the head as a ram or scraper. Similarly, in order to inspect those turns on the winch that have been used in the course of platform positioning, the winch tension is slackened by around ten tonnes before inspection begins.

When it is necessary to inspect the mooring line below the fairlead, the head is positioned and attached by air divers. In this case only 45 m of the mooring can be inspected, as there are distance and depth restrictions on divers who may be required to detach the head from the mooring if it becomes stuck.

With the equipment ready, the winch is started and the head is pulled up the cable at a (nominally) constant velocity. Speed compensation circuits are included in the signal conditioning to adjust to minor speed variations due to fluctuating winch air pressure and to progressive errors such as coiling of cable on the winch drums.

Head speed relative to the mooring is measured using a jockey wheel which sends out 16 electrical pulses per revolution and is clamped to the edge of the winch drum. The speed compensation circuitry continually adjusts the channel gain applied to the signals from the sensor coils. This is because the amplitude of a signal for a given defect will increase with the speed of the rope past the coils.

If necessary, a mooring can be reinspected by simply lowering the head back down the mooring to its start position and repeating the process. This may be required to confirm or clarify an unusual trace. Each inspection typically takes only a few minutes, apart from the time involved in initial equipment positioning and set-up.

INSPECTION RESULTS

The received signals from each run are stored as magnetic recordings and also as paper chart traces. Defects such as wire breaks, corrosion and abrasion produce characteristic signal traces, and assessment of an inspection run can be simplified by using a rope defect monitor, which provides a numeric assessment of the categories of defect present.

Calibration

The equipment is calibrated on a short section of mooring line containing a known range of defects. The internal coil sensitivity is adjusted so that at a relative rope speed of 0.5 m/s, a single wire break will produce a 100 mV signal on the chart recorder. The Hall effect sensors are calibrated statically using steel rods of various known diameters. Figure 3a shows the calibration traces from the sensor coils and the Hall sensor array. The defects in the mooring section are: one length of bent-over wire, a 5 mm wire gap and overlay, a single wire break, two wire breaks (10 mm gap) and two wire breaks (50 mm gap). The Hall sensor trace is subject to end effects.

Inspection Traces

Two traces from in-situ inspections of mooring lines are shown in Fig 3.

Figure 3b shows a single wire break on the mooring line. The defect was subsequently found to lie on the surface on the rope.

Figure 3c shows the increase in the baseline 'noise' level, probably due to internal damage to the independent wire rope core (IWRC).

FUTURE EQUIPMENT DEVELOPMENT

BP are considering development of the NDT technology from the prototype stage into a rugged, computer based, purpose-built inspection system, capable of adaption to varied inspection requirements which might include crane ropes, diving bell wires, TLP tethers, armoured umbilicals, riser tension wires etc. The system would be suitable for land or marine use by non-specialist operators and the computer based data acquisition and analysis system will enable configuration to meet many specific inspection requirements.

To meet future deepwater inspection requirements, the NDT equipment would need to be capable of remote operation from the surface. In such circumstances, it would be operationally and economically unsuitable to employ umbilicals past shallow water depths.

A remotely operated tractor unit has been designed, for deepwater use. This unit would pull the existing NDT sensor head along a tether. It would operate without an umbilical cable and would communicate with the surface using a multi-channel sonar link. The design incorporates an automatic release mechanism which, in the event of the unit becoming stuck or upon failure of the on-board power supply, would allow the unit to float to the surface for retrieval.

The use of ROV's for deployment of an autonomous system could benefit those areas which currently rely on visual surface inspection of subsea components by the ROV's operator.

CONCLUSIONS

BP has developed an NDT device, in collaboration with Mera-Ster of Poland, suitable for subsea inspection of large diameter steel wire ropes.

The system has been successfully used offshore for in-situ, non-destructive inspection of Buchan Alpha's moorings.

Annual use of the system has been written into the Operations Manual of the platform and the results are used as part of the assessment of the lifetime of each mooring. This allows BP to confidently maximise the service lives of the moorings - resulting in fewer change-outs and significant financial savings.

Future work could involve making the present system more rugged and may require development of an autonomous deepwater device.

ACKNOWLEDGEMENTS

The author gratefully acknowledges the work by Mr P Robinson of the BP Research Centre in developing the prototype wire rope inspection system, and thanks the British Petroleum Company plc for permission to publish this paper.

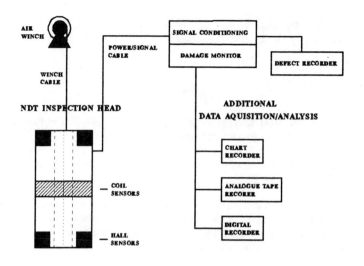

Fig 1   NDT system schematic

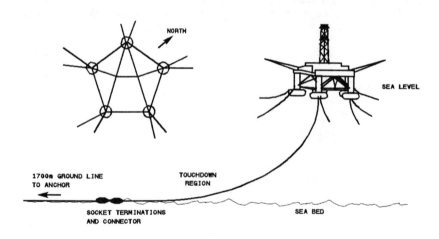

Fig 2   Buchan Alpha anchor line layout

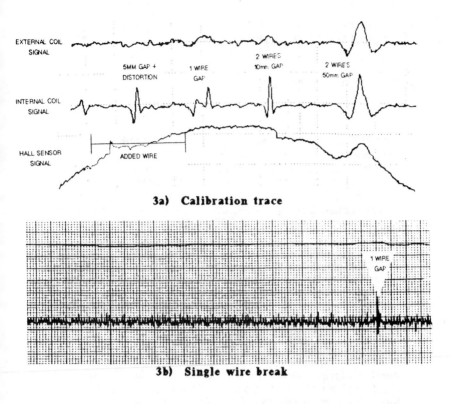

3a) Calibration trace

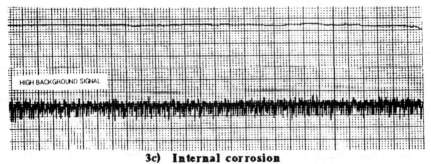

3b) Single wire break

3c) Internal corrosion

Fig 3   Inspection traces

A CASE FOR ELECTROMAGNETIC NDT INSPECTION OF MULTISTRAND DIVING BELL HOIST ROPES

A.E. POTTS AND C.R. CHAPLIN

Current recommendations issued by the Department of Energy for the maintenance, inspection and discard criteria for multistrand diving bell hoist ropes include periodic visual inspection and test loading, with six monthly tailing and retirement after a set period in service, irrespective of condition. A series of bending-over-sheave fatigue tests using a variety of multistrand rope constructions indicated that these types of rope deteriorate internally long before there are external signs of degradation. Current visual inspection procedures and discard criteria recommended in ISO 4309 and BS 6570 do not address these internal deterioration mechanisms in multistrand ropes adequately and may be dangerously misleading by giving insufficient warning of imminent rope failure. Two multistrand diving bell hoist ropes retired after a number of years service in the North Sea were inspected, using electromagnetic NDT devices. Selected sections of the rope were subsequently dismantled to correlate the rope condition with the NDT signal trace; and also to check that the same deterioration mechanisms seen in the fatigue tests were evident. The use of electromagnetic inspection devices would improve condition monitoring of these ropes and, in conjunction with more suitable discard criteria for multistrand ropes, should provide the basis for safely extending service lives with confidence.

INTRODUCTION

The recent development of major offshore oil and gas fields has lead to a dramatic increase in diving operations. Prior to this, up to the mid-1960's, saturation diving techniques using diving bells were well established, although most diving activities were confined to work in harbours and salvage operations in water depths up to 70-80 metres. The advent of North Sea oil provided a large amount of regular diving work on construction and servicing (i.e. maintenance and repair) of offshore platforms, subsea pipelines and other associated installations. Since the mid-1970's North Sea diving operations have regularly involved saturation diving at depths up to 140 metres. In the

Department of Engineering, University of Reading,
Whiteknights, P.O. Box 225, Reading, Berkshire, RG6 2AY, UK.

UK sector of the North Sea alone, there are about 50 diving spreads (i.e. individual diving hoist systems) operating from fixed and mobile platforms, multi-function service vessels and diving support vessels.

Diving bell operations put great onus on the integrity of the ropes used for lowering and raising manned diving bells, particularly in saturation diving, where the divers are effectively trapped in the artificial atmosphere of the bell. The incidence of diving bell hoist rope failures is small and not widely reported, although from the three known accidents (one of which occurred in the UK sector of the North Sea), five persons lost their lives (Giles (1)).

Diving bell hoists typically use multistrand ropes, although the arrangement of the diving bell lifting mechanisms and the nature of offshore operations ensure that the ropes have entirely different loading and environmental exposure conditions to onshore lifting applications using the same rope constructions. Current statutory requirements and guidelines for recommended practice issued to the diving industry by the UK Department of Energy – Diving Inspectorate are open and somewhat imprecise. They recommend that the hoist ropes be periodically inspected by established visual examination procedures and proof loaded in-situ, with six monthly tailing and retirement after a set period in service, irrespective of condition. Many within the diving industry consider that hoist ropes could be kept in service for longer periods without endangering divers' safety. It was recognised that new operating guidelines on maintenance and inspection procedures and discard criteria were required, which were based on a sound understanding of rope behaviour and operational experience, in order to assess and, if possible, increase the safe working life of these ropes.

In response the Department of Energy commissioned a series of studies initially at British Ropes Ltd., and subsequently at the University of Reading, where work continues. A programme of bending-over-sheave (BOS) fatigue tests on six different multistrand ropes constructions were performed at British Ropes Ltd. (2), four of which were later examined at Reading (Chaplin and Walton (3)) in order to:
  (i)   determine the typical BOS fatigue life of multistrand ropes under diving bell hoist loading and bending conditions;
  (ii)   determine the applicability of established visual inspection wire break discard criteria; and,
  (iii) assess the type, location and degree of damage and the fatigue mechanisms operating within the rope.

Following this, two diving bell hoist ropes retired from service in the North Sea with known details of operation, were examined both visually and with NDT by Reading (Chaplin and others (4)), to:
  (i)   assess the condition of ropes being maintained and discarded in accordance with current guidelines;
  (ii)   determine the locations and causes of rope degradation; and,

(iii)   comment upon the safety and applicability of current maintenance and inspection guidelines, recommending alternatives as necessary.

The current work at Reading is concentrating on providing a basis for future guide-lines and involves:

(i)   surveying diving vessel operators and inspecting diving vessels to determine the types of winding arrangements, deployment procedures and the maintenance, inspection and discard policy for the hoist ropes;

(ii)   evaluating a range of NDT equipment using samples of diving bell rope with various types of service damage and samples with artificially introduced defects; and,

(iii)   evaluating available pressure re-lubrication systems.

This paper discusses the findings from the earlier work and presents a case for the regular use of electromagnetic NDT devices for inspecting multistrand diving bell hoist ropes which, in conjunction with more suitable maintenance procedures and discard criteria, should provide the basis for safely extending the service lives of these ropes with confidence.

MULTISTRAND ROPES

Diving bell hoist ropes are typically 25-35 mm. diameter with a high proportion being 35 x 7 dyeformed construction, although different constructions and larger diameters are in use on some installations.

Multistrand ropes are highly flexible and, as their name suggests, comprise of two or more layers of strands, in which the outer strands are laid in the opposite direction to the inner layer(s) to provide torque balancing, i.e. limited rotation under load. A cut-away section of multistrand rope is shown in Fig. 1, along with a number of cross-sections of different multistrand ropes. The strands are typically made of seven round wires, although dyeformed strands and more complex strand constructions are also common.

Interstrand and pulley groove contact stresses are less severe with dyeforming, resulting in superior fatigue endurance over round wire constructions. Lang's lay outer strands also have lower pulley groove bearing stresses which usually improves BOS fatigue performance over ordinary lay ropes.

The torque balanced characteristics of the rope are provided and lay by the direction of strands in the rope. However, the severity of fretting conditions within the rope is a function of both radical loads and the cross-over angle between outer wires of the strands in contact. The higher the angle, the more severe since the bearing area will be smaller and thus contact stresses will be higher. Table 1 sets out the severity of inter-wire cross-over angles between outer wires of strands of different lays and direction of lay. The low contact angles occur when the wires are almost parallel, whereas very high contact angles are virtually at right angles.

DIVING BELL HOIST ROPES LOADING CONDITIONS

Diving bell hoisting systems vary from spread to spread, although many use a cursor arrangement for supporting the bell in air to just below the waterline, below which the bell is suspended from just the single rope. Multistrand ropes are selected for their flexibility and their torque balancing which prevents the bell from freely rotating. The cursor frame supporting the bell passes down a trackway through the waterline, inhibiting any violent lateral movement of the bell in this zone. Figure 2 shows the hoisting system arrangement on one of the diving vessels from which Reading received a retired rope. The multi-fall rope reeving system shown gives a mechanical advantage of 3:1 in lifting the bell and cursor. Peak tensions due to vessel and wave motions can be reduced with the use of a heave motion compensator in the hoisting system and with diving operations carried out through a moon pool.

DSM 8/1977 (5) issued by the Department of Energy specifies a minimum factor of safety (FOS) of 4 with a 2g dynamic load factor such that the maximum allowable load is MBL/4 and the safe working load (SWL) is MBL/8, where MBL is the manufacturer's rated minimum breaking load for the rope. DSM 5/1982 (6) and DSM 17/1982 (7) define the safe working load as the total weight of the bell in air at water level (i.e. including maximum cable weight) when operationally manned. When submerged, the buoyant weight of the diving bell is about 10% to 20% of its weight in air, thus providing a nominal "Lifting Appliances - Classification" (8). ISO 4308-1981, "Cranes - Selection of Wire Ropes" (9) recommends that the minimum bending D/d (pulley diameter over rope diameter) ratios for Class M5 lifting mechanisms are 18:1 for winches and 20:1 for pulleys. These 'fairly tight' bending conditions are typical of those used in bell hoist systems.

In diving operations, the hoist rope will be subjected to three regimes of fatigue loading along its length when lowering and lifting the bell:

(i)   the length of rope nearest the bell which supports the bell and cursor in air will experience BOS fatigue at a FOS of about 8;

(ii) the short length of rope at the contact with the first pulley above the bell when the bell passes through the waterline will experience bending-tension (B-T) fatigue due to buoyancy effects and dynamic amplication due to waves and vessel motions with loads fluctuating between FOS of 4 and 25; and,

(iii) the remaining length of rope when the bell is fully submerged will be subject to very light BOS fatigue at a FOS of about 25.

Bending-over-sheave fatigue is the conventional form of rope fatigue loading where long lengths of rope are drawn over a pulley under effectively constant tension. Bending-tension fatigue occurs when very short lengths of rope (including rope stretch) are subject to flexure on and off the pulley in phase with fluctuating tensile loads. Very few tests have been performed to model this form of fatigue loading, however it is considered to be a more severe regime than BOS fatigue for a given bending length. When the bell is submerged, B-T fatigue may also occur around pulleys when there is no heave compensation mechanism.

ENVIRONMENTAL EXPOSURE CONDITIONS

The environmental exposure conditions relate to the corrosion performance of the rope which is of particular concern in the aggressive marine environment.

North Sea diving operations usually only occur in long periods of fair weather, which confines most operations to summer diving seasons. During this period diving may take place at regular time intervals to maintain continuous subsea work shifts. In these operations, the hoist ropes are subject to short periods of raising and lowering (i.e. BOS fatigue) only, although they may be submerged in seawater under relatively constant load for long periods of time (of the order of six hours per dive).

During dives, protection of the rope against the ingress of seawater and associated corrosion assisted fretting-fatigue is supplied by a heavy marine grade lubricant/ blocking compound and/or galvanised wires. Surprisingly, not all diving bell hoist ropes are galvanised, nor is their any requirement for them to be so. Additional protection may be provided if the diving vessel operates an impressed current cathodic protection system with sufficient 'throw'. Conversely if the system is inoperable and there is insufficient back-up protection from sacrificial anodes, the galvanising on the rope will act as such for both rope and vessel and be rapidly dissolved.

Between dives and out of the diving season, the ropes are stored on the hoisting winches. Depending upon the state and effectiveness of the rope lubricant/blocking compound, trapped seawater within the rope's construction can provide active corrosion conditions, which will be particularly severe for ungalvanised ropes.

CURRENT RECOMMENDED PRACTICE FOR DIVING BELL HOIST ROPES

The statutory requirement covering maintenance of diving bell plant and equipment are set out in the Health and Safety Act - Diving Operations at Work Regulations (SI No. 399, part 13, 1981 (10)) and do not specifically refer to the hoist ropes. The inspection and maintenance requirements for diving bell hoist ropes are embodied in the general clauses which specify that diving plant and equipment shall not be used unless:
   (i)   "it is maintained in a condition which will ensure so far as is reasonably practicable that it is safe while it is being used"; and,
   (ii) "it has been examined by a competent person within the six hours immediately before the diving operation commenced".

The Department of Energy–Diving Inspectorate issues guidance recommendations to the industry in the form of Diving Safety Memoranda (DSM). DSM's are not regulations per se, but set out recommended standards and practices which are incorporated in certification society requirements (e.g. Lloyd's Register of Shipping, "Code for Lifting Appliances in a Marine Environment" (11)).

DSM 5/1982 (6) and DSM 17/1982 (7), which superseded it, recommended that the lifting system be tested and examined on initial installation, after any major repair or alterations to the plant or equipment, and at six monthly intervals. On these occasions the hoist rope was to be test loaded to a specified proof load of 1.5 x SWL.

British Ropes Ltd. (12) prepared written guidance notes on socketing, installation and maintenance of diving bell hoist ropes, which the Department of Energy later issued to the diving industry for consideration in 1986. These guidance notes recommend that diving bell hoist ropes should be replaced every two years irrespective of condition or service and that during this period:

(i)   the ropes should be visually inspected at regular intervals by a competent person for wear, defects/broken wires, corrosion or mechanical damage in accordance with ISO 4309 - 1981 (13) and BS 6570:1986 (14);

(ii) frequent dressings should be applied manually or by an automatic system e.g. every 10-14 days, and on every occasion prior to diving operations being suspended for a period of time;

(iii) ropes should be tailed and re-terminated every six months (the length to be determined by the 'competent person'); and,

(iv) before being re-socketed, a length of approximately 2 metres should be cut off adjacent to the socket for later detailed examination and tensile testing to establish the residual breaking strength.

Robertson (15) points out that it was agreed with diving operators that the recommended service life may be extended to three years, if the rope was periodically pressure re-lubricated. No detailed guidance covering this point was issued, nor any recommendations addressing type of device and dressing to be used, the degree of penetration or the frequency of application.

The British Ropes Ltd. guidance notes (11) recommended against the practice of annually 'end-for-ending' the hoist rope. It was considered that operations associated with 'end-for-ending' (i.e. winching the rope on and off reels a number of times), if not properly controlled, could often damage rotation resistant ropes by introducing torque imbalances (e.g. birdcaging or waviness).

The two to three year recommended service life is similar to that specified for friction winder mine hoist ropes which are typically of either locked coil or multistrand construction (NCB Ropeman's Handbook (10)). However there are significant differences between these applications which do not justify the same discard policy. Friction winder ropes operate at higher loads (minimum FOS of 4.5 at deep depths and 6.5 at surface), winding speeds are much higher (typically 8 m/s as opposed to 1 m/s), the frequency of use is orders of magnitude higher, but bending ratios are much more benign (D/d of 100:1 or more), and although winding rope sometimes operate in 'wet' shafts, there is no seawater to contend with. It should be noted that the coal mining regulations require winding ropes operating in wet shafts or similarly corrosive environments to be manufactured from galvanized wire. Also the removal of sample lengths from friction winder ropes for testing and examination when periodically re-terimating is impractical due to the requirement for an effectively constant length.

APPLICABILITY OF VISIBLE WIRE BREAK DISCARD CRITERIA

ISO 4309-1981 (13) and BS 6570:1986 (14) set out examination procedures and discard criteria for visually inspecting steel wire ropes. The decision to discard a rope may be based on the individual and combined levels of:

(i)   mechanical damage (e.g. kinking, crushing, birdcaging and plucking);
(ii)   corrosion;
(iii)   abrasion and wear; and,
(iv)   concentrations of visible broken wires.

Mechanical damage is usually clearly visible and straightforward to detect, although wire plucking, usually associated with multi-layer winch drums, can be more difficult to detect, as it mostly takes the form of isolated areas of damage (i.e. one or two broken wires) occurring at set intervals along the rope. Distributed losses of metallic cross-sectional area of the rope due to corrosion, abrasion and wear can be visually detected by a number of signs, such as red iron oxide, flattening of outer wires, and loss, or sometimes, increase in rope diameter. However, it is much more difficult to quantify the actual loss in metallic area, and therefore estimate the loss in rope strength from visual examination procedures.

The incidence of external wire breaks is different from the other forms of rope deterioration as it is principally a function of BOS fatigue cycling from the rope running on and off pulleys and winch drums. Wire breaks will occur within the rope at locations of high cyclic contact fretting-fatigue, such as between wires and between outer wires and pulleys. For most parallel lay stranded rope constructions (i.e. six and eight strand ropes) operating under typical working conditions (i.e. recommended FOS and D/d ratios) the outer wire-pulley contact stresses are most severe, and failure is precipitated by a concentration of external breaks due to these stresses. In such cases, the use of numbers of external wire breaks as a discard criterion gives adequate indication of impending rope failure.

The codes of practice specify that ropes should be discarded if a certain number of visible external wire breaks within a set length of rope is exceeded. Table 2 sets out the ISO 4309-1981 (13) and BS 6570:1986 (14) visible wire break discard criteria for various multistrand rope constructions operating under typical diving bell hoist loading conditions (i.e. FOS > 5 and D/d of about 18-25). ISO 4309-1981 makes different allowances for Lang's and ordinary lay ropes and specifies two allowable levels of wire break concentrations (i.e. in 6d and 30d).

Table 3 sets out the results from the programme of BOS fatigue tests on six different 14mm diameter multistrand ropes (different constructions and manufacturers), performed at British Ropes Ltd. (2). The ropes were fatigued at a FOS of 5 (i.e. FOS 90° contact angle = MBL/5) and D/d of 20:1 over 'kind' pulleys (i.e. fine grain cast iron) with no fleet angle. The bending stroke used in these tests was 450mm (i.e. 32d) and as such that two sections of rope were subjected to twice the number of bending cycles experienced by other sections. Accordingly, failure always occurred along one of these sections. The tests were stopped every 500 cycles to count the number of external wire breaks along these sections to monitor the progress of visible fatigue deterioration.

Comparisons of the relative fatigue performance of each construction is difficult due to the likely but unknown differences in margin between MBL and actual tensile strength. Although comparisons between the 35 x 7 constructions from ropemaker C indicate that dyeformed constructions have superior BOS fatigue performance, and that there is no significant difference between Lang's and ordinary lay ropes at these load and bending conditions.

The 18 x 7 construction, with the largest round wires (i.e. the most severe outer wire-pulley contact stresses), was the only rope for which the discard criterion was consistently reached before failure. For the others the criterion was detected before failure in only a third of the tests. On these occasions it was detected earlier on the round wire constructions than the dyeformed wires. It should be noted that the low incidence of external wire breaks may to some degree have been influenced by the fairly 'soft' pulleys used in the tests.

Even in view of this latter point, it is apparent from Table 3 that the visible external wire break discard criteria specified in ISO 4309-1981 (13) and also BS 6570:1986 (14) for multi-strand ropes do not provide sufficient indication of impending failure. Consequently, it is considered unsafe to rely upon this form of discard criteria for multistrand ropes used in man riding applications.

FATIGUE MECHANISMS IN MULTISTRAND ROPES

A representative sample of four of the rope constructions tested were dismantled and examined in detail at Reading to identify the fatigue mechanisms and how they differ, if at all, between constructions. Two round wire and two dyeformed wire constructions were chosen.

A 400mm length of rope, which had been subject to the same number of bending cycles as the failure location (indicated in Fig. 3), was sectioned for subsequent dismantling. During the stripping down of the layers the numbers and locations of internal and external wire breaks were noted and various photographs taken. A summary of the number of wire breaks counted on the rope exterior and internal strand layer interfaces for a 400mm section of rope is presented in Table 4. Also presented are the strand construction details (i.e. strands per layer and direction of lay) and cross-over angles of wires at the strand layer interfaces.

Except for the 18 x 7 multistrand with the larger round wires, most of the wire breaks occurred at the interface between outer and second layer of strands. Figure 4 shows a section of the 35 x 7 (LHL) dyeformed multistrand rope with a few of the outer strands (which showed no visible external damage) removed to reveal extensive break-up on the outer surface of the second layer. The number and distribution of internal wire breaks is about the same for each of the 35 x 7 constructions, indicating the same relative loss in constructional strength at failure.

The details of the mechanisms leading to internal fractures are highly dependent on the nature of the relative crossing angles between wires in the strands in adjacent layers. Figures 5 to 8 show examples of typical damage associated with the inter-wire cross-over angles between wires in adjacent strands (i.e. very high through to low cross–over angles).

The issue as to whether this form of fatigue degradation (i.e. concentrated at the outer and second strand layer interface) is a product of the test conditions, or actually occurs in service, is settled with Fig. 9. This shows a multistrand crane whipline rope removed from service on an offshore platform, that exhibited little external signs of fatigue damage, but with extensive break-up on the second layer. It should be noted that crane whiplines experience more bending cycles at lower FOS than diving bell hoist ropes; however, if diving bell hoist rope lives are extended without check or on the basis of good external condition, then such levels of damage will inevitably occur.

EXAMINATION OF RETIRED DIVING BELL HOIST ROPES

By arrangement with the Department of Energy, two recently retired diving bell hoist ropes (minus terminations) of known origins and service history, used on diving vessels operating in the UK sector of the North Sea were provided for detailed examination and testing. Details on rope construction and service and maintenance history are summarised in Table 5.

Using a mechanical spooling facility at British Ropes Ltd., Doncaster, the ropes were wound at a controlled rate initially for visual examination and then inspection using electromagnetic NDT equipment. Polish manufactured Mera-Ster GP-1 (for 30 mm to 85 mm ø ropes) and GP-2 (for 20 mm to 60 mm ø ropes) measuring heads with an MD-12 Defectoscope and Gould Brush 222 signal recording equipment were used for the NDT work. The permanent magnet NDT devices were measuring stray flux leakage related to localised damage such as broken wires, severe localised corrosion and wear and construction distortions. The devices were not able to detect distributed losses of metallic area due to corrosion or abrasion (NB: in the case of the GP-1 head, the metallic area circuitry was inoperable at the time). Areas of significant damage along the ropes were identified with the NDT equipment and marked for later sectioning as test samples or dismantling and detailed examination.

The first 35-40m from the bell end in each of the ropes showed the most active NDT signal trace, consistent with the heavier duty of lifting the bell and cursor in air (NB: the length of rope from which to bell when the bell is at the water interface was about 40-50 m). Figure 10 presents two sections (0-30 m and 80-90 m) of condensed NDT signal trace for Rope 1, showing the different levels of signal activity along these sections, and indicating the types of damage identified for various signal disturbances. The fibrillated and missing wires (Figs. 11 and 12) which were clearly detected can mostly be attributed to the multi-layer Lebus-type winch arrangement. Little or no internal damage was detected other than some slight wear and crushing, mostly confined to the smaller wires in the second layer filler strands.

Much of the damage detected with the NDT equipment was not found from visual examination mostly due to the heavy lubricant covering the outside of the rope which obscured all but protruding wire breaks. This situation is made even worse when corrosion products are combined with the lubricant, such as occurred with Rope 2.

The level of corrosion was evenly distributed along the entire length of Rope 1. Tests were performed in accordance with BS 443:1982 (17) to determine the amount of remaining zinc on the wires which wer then compared with the minimum specified coating thickness for Class Z galvanising (BS 2763:1982 (18)). The outer wires had 10% remaining, the second layer 25%, the third 45% with all zinc intact on the core strand. This even distribution of corrosion is consistent with having been end-for-ended during life. Rope 2, on the other hand, was heavily corroded (i.e. about 8% zinc remaining in all layers) in the first half of length, the next 60 m was partially corroded (i.e. slightly more zinc than on Rope 1), with virtually all zinc intact on the remaining last third of length. This degree of corrosion is believed to be as a result of the vessel's impressed current cathodic protection system being turned-off during diving operations, such that the zinc on the rope acted as a sacrificial anode to the whole vessel and rapidly dissolved. The uncorroded end is consistent with never having been submerged and remaining on the winch.

Residual strength tests were performed on representative samples from each of the ropes which, along with the rated catalogue MBL and as new test strengths, are presented in Table 5. it is interesting to note that the as-new ropes are some 4% to 7% weaker than the catalogue rated MBL for that size and construction. The breaking load of undamage rope samples that have seen service exceeds the MBL's, which is probably due to better load sharing among wires from bedding-in and increased internal friction from loss of lubricant and corrosion products.

DISCUSSION

In making recommendations as to what constitues a safe working life for diving bell hoist ropes, or on what basis a rope should be retired from service, a number of factors must be considered, including:

(i)   condition of ropes being discarded under the current maintenance, inspection and discard policy;

(ii) the sources of damage;

(iii) the types of damage likely with extended service; and,

(iv) the availability of reliable means of inspecting ropes to detect degradation and to assess the servicable condition of the rope (i.e. residual strength and remaining fatigue life).

It should be noted that the lengths of rope retired from each diving vessel was about 190 m less than that purchased (Table 5). No information was available on the actual length of rope originally fitted or the lengths removed when cut-and-slipping, although the lengths missing is consistent with some 40–50 m being removed every six months in service. Accordingly, there is uncertainty about what proportion of full service life the various sections of hoist rope have experienced. It is most likely that that the length nearest the bell, which experiences the heaviest duty, had been in that position for only a year since the tailing and re-terminating operation prior to discard. Consequently, some reservations must be expressed regarding conclusions relating to the condition of sections of the rope immediately adjacent to the bell.

The forms of rope degradation detected in the retired ropes were broken outer wires due to mechanical damage and corrosion, with only very early indications of the onset of fatigue (i.e. the presence of wire indentations and some localised crushing at severe cross-over locations). Most of the degradation occurred in the 30–40 m of rope nearest the bell, which most probably represents damage accrued over only one year.

The number of BOS cycles experienced by the ropes over their entire service periods (Table 5) were less than half of the fatigue test endurances to failure of similar ropes under more severe conditions (i.e. FOS = 5 and D/d = 20 in tests, FOS = 8-10 and D/d = 21-22 in service). The lack of internal fatigue damage in the retired hoist ropes, of the sort found in the sections of BOS test ropes, is consistent with the low proportion of fatigue life experienced. Note however, that an even smaller proportion of BOS life would have been experienced if, as seems likely, the ropes were tailed as far back as the winch each year. Extended service lives of up to 4 or 5 years, even with minimal tailing, are unlikely to give rise to significant levels of fatigue damage (such as shown in Figs. 4 and 9), except where large heave compensation motions around pulleys are regularly involved with continual operations at the same depths.

The mechanical damage sustained by the ropes was mostly due to winching problems (i.e. plucking and crushing of wires at cross-over points of ropes wound on multi-layer winches) and pulley fleet angles. It should be noted that these sources of damage may be avoided or minimised to a large extent through better hoisting system design. Also pulling-in of the winch end of the rope will move the rope cross-over points which are subject to this repetitive damage, distributing its effect and thereby reducing its severity. Even so, the loss of rope strength of the sections of Rope 1 damaged in this way (Table 5) were at worst only 5% less than the as new test strength. Extended service lives on un-modified systems producing the same types of damage would give cause for rope discard in only one or two diving seasons. With modified hoising systems and/or improved maintenance practices, far greater service lives may be achieved.

The incidence of corrosion in both ropes was very much a function of operating and maintenance practices as well. The heavy loss of zinc on the bell end of Rope 2 due to it acting as a sacrificial anode for both the rope and diving vessel is simply avoided by keeping the vessel's impressed current cathodic protection system on during diving operations, as it poses no safety threat to divers. The high percentage of original zinc coating thickness lost on the outer strand layers of Rope 1 was due to prolonged exposure of the wires to to seawater and the marine environment. This may be attributed to the state of the rope lubricant. The service re-lubrication/dressing had only penetrated the outer layers and further inside the rope, the original lubricant had dried-out and been displaced allowing corrosion to occur, most probably accelerated by trapped seawater. The loss of zinc had not weakened the rope, as corrosion had not yet attacked the base metal. However, extending the service period of such a rope unchecked may give rise to serious localised weakening of the rope.

Corrosion will always occur to a certain extent, whether it be in the form of direct attack on the steel wires or loss of the zinc coating. Significant corrosion may on bright new ropes even in storage and will be particularly rapid when exposed to the more aggressive marine environment, although good lubrication can provide a degree of protection. The surest way to minimize the influence of corrosion is for all diving bell hoist ropes to be heavy galvanized (i.e. at least Class Z, BS 2763:1982 (18) or heavier), which is usually only some 7% more expensive than bright. Also, the periodic use of effective pressure re-lubrication that fully penetrates the dense multistrand contruction, in addition to regular service dressing (e.g. running the rope through a lubricant bath), will reduce the rate of zinc loss and thereby further protect the rope against corrosion

The concentration of most of the damage in the 30-40 m length of rope nearest the bell, whether accrued over one or many years service, may suggest a maintenance policy of periodic tailing of the entire length from the bell at water level up to the first pulley, or even as far as the winch. In many cases this would be both inappropriate and wasteful, and if service lives were extended beyond present limits, this would lead to rope discard due to insufficient remaining length, rather than rope condition.

In hoisting systems where the forms of external mechanical damage and advanced corrosion, as seen in the two retired ropes, have been minimized, it may not be necessary to tail long lengths of rope and safe working lives could be extended with confidence, until rope condition necessitates discard. In such circumstances, other forms of rope degradation will become more apparent, such as external and internal wear and abrasion and internal wire break-up due to fatigue. It is apparent from the BOS fatigue tests performed, that reliance on the the the conventional visible external wire break discard criteria for multistrand ropes can be very dangerous due to the concealed internal fatigue break-up that occurs. Loss of metallic cross-sectional area of these ropes due to corrosion, wear and/or abrasion can also be difficult to detect and quantify, particularly when predominantly internal.

Electromagnetic NDT devices would seem to be the only available, reliable method of detecting both external and internal forms of damage on multistrand ropes. The trials performed on the two retired diving bell hoist ropes showed that external broken wires (both isolated and concentrated) could be more readily detected with NDT than by visual techniques, as well as picking-up less pronounced constructional irregularities and to a limited extent, deformed internal wires. The detection of damage and identification of its type and extent does however depend upon the equipment. The NDT equipment used were permanent magnet devices capable of detecting localised flaws only. Ideally, NDT equipment for regular in-service inspections should also incorporate some means of measuring distributed losses in metallic cross-sectional area such as due to corrosion, wear and abrasion.

At present levels of understanding, NDT devices should be initially used as a supplement to visual inspections. With greater experience of use with multistrand ropes (i.e. both in-service inspections and through testing such as that being carried-out at Reading) this role may be extended, such that visual examination takes a more confirmatory role.

The capabilities of NDT devices varies between manufacturers (depending upon magnetic field saturations achieved, sensor types and arrangements and signal processing equipment), and as such it is virtually impossible to specify universal discard criteria based on signal levels alone. In addition, what the signal is indicating (i.e. the type, degree and location of damage), which may differ between devices and rope contructions, relies heavily on the interpretive skills of inspection personnel. Accordingly, discard criteria for use with NDT equipment should be performance related i.e. based on perceived loss of rope mechanical properties. This judgement must consider external as well as internal levels of damage/deterioration detected visually and/or by NDT, rather than just visible external signs of degradation.

Most codes of practice for rope examination, including ISO 4309-1981 (13) and BS 6570:1986 (14), have not addressed the use of electromagnetic NDT equipment for assessing rope condition. The US standard for mining ropes, ANSI M11.1-1980 (19), regards existing NDT devices as supplementary tools and recommend that they should be used only as an adjunct to visual inspection in the following manner:

(i)   NDT inspections should be performed at least every 4 to 6 months;

(ii)   NDT records should be compared with the as-new and previous records to determine the rate of changes in rope condition and to make estimates of strength loss in damaged areas;

(iii)   ropes should be visually examined wherever the NDT record indicates a developing weakness or an obvious peculiarity;

(iv)   removal should be considered if results of NDT indicate a strength loss of 10% or more at any point, whether or not anything is visible at those points; and,

(v)   as good practice, tensile tests should be performed on sample lengths of rope, particularly damaged sections, to compare with strengths estimated from NDT and to provide a continuing basis for instrument and technique development.

The part of the Lloyd's Code of Practice (11) dealing with ship lift systems also considers the use of electromagnetic NDT equipment for assessing the condition of the lift ropes. As a pre-cursor to the regular use of these devices in-service it sets out the requirement that field tests must be carried-out to verify the accuracy, reliability and suitability of the NDT equipment for the particular rope, hoist arrangement and rope speed. The associated discard criteria specified includes:

(i)   the number of broken wires in any 10 d length exceeds 5% of the total number of wires;

(ii)   the cross-sectional area is reduced by more than 10% of the original area; and,

(iii)   the reduction in rope breaking strength, when the combined effect of metal loss, corrosion pitting and broken wires has been taken into account, exceeds 10 %MBL.

Although the wire break discard criterion makes no discrimination between visible external and internal breaks, it is presumed that it is the same as the visible external wire break criterion referred to in most rope examination codes of practice.

By specifying both loss of area and loss of strength as discard criteria, the Lloyd's Code of Practice recognises that strength loss is not always directly proportional to the loss in metallic cross-sectional area. In the case of multistrand ropes, the concentration of a small number of breaks or some localised wear or corrosion may disrupt the torque balancing of the construction and result in strength losses significantly greater than the proportion of reduced metallic area at that cross-section. Any estimates of strength loss with multistrand ropes requires an understanding of the individual and combined effects of various types of defects and their location in the rope cross-section. Their is no published guidance on this subject for multistand ropes and it clearly requires further investigation. Estimates of strength loss will therefore depend greatly upon the advise of ropemakers and ultimately the judgement and experience of the rope examiner.

CONCLUSIONS

The conclusions from this work may be summarised as follows:

(i)   Multistrand ropes subject to BOS fatigue loading, such as occurs in hoisting applications, will primarily break-up on the interface between the outer and second layer of strands concealed from view.

(ii)   The visible external wire break discard criteria for multistrand ropes specified in ISO 4309-1981 (13) and BS 6570:1986 (14), do not give adequate indication of pending rope failure and can therefore be highly dangerous, if solely relied upon for deciding discard on man riding installations.

(iii) The retired diving bell hoist ropes examined, which were used under current inspection and maintenance guidelines, did not exhibit fatigue break-up, but instead localised mechanical damage and corrosion.

(iv)   Most of the mechanical damage could be attributed to winding problems on multi-layer winch drums and excessive fleet angles, which could be minimized with better hoisting system design and periodic pulling-in of the winch-end of the rope on the drum.

(v)   All diving bell hoist ropes should be heavy galvanised and supplied with an appropriate marine grade lubricant. Where under normal circumstances (i.e. the galvanizing on the rope is not acting as a sacrificial anode to both the rope and diving vessel), the rate of zinc loss may be reduced and therefore the corrosion life of the rope extended with periodic effective pressure re–lubrication, in addition to regular dressing of the rope.

(vi)   The concentration of mechanical damage and corrosion in the 30-40 m length of rope nearest the bell suggests that the hoist rope should be periodically tailed from the bell at water level back to just beyond the first pulley, if not all the way back to the winch. If however, the sources of mechanical damage are minimized and the rate of corrosion reduced with regular rope dressing and periodic pressure re-lubrication, such long lengths need not necessarily be removed.

(vii) The general condition of the ropes examined suggested that the 2 to 3 year recommended maximum service life is probably too conservative for well maintained galvanized ropes. If service lives are extended beyond 2 to 3 years, with limited tailing, there is a higher likelihood of significant internal rope degradation through fatigue break-up, wear and corrosion, which cannot be detected or quantified by standard visual examination procedures.

(viii) The use of electromagnetic NDT devices in conjunction with visual examination will greatly aid the detection and definition of both external and internal forms of damage on multistrand ropes. Thereby providing the means for safely extending the service life of diving bell hoist ropes until rope condition, rather than specified service period, necessitates discard.

(ix) Rope performance related discard ctiteria, such as those set out in Lloyd's Code of Practice (11), are considered suitable for use with NDT devices in this application. The decision to discard will still rely greatly on the judgement of the rope examiner in interpreting the NDT signal and assessing the individual and combined influence of the rope defects detected.

ACKNOWLEDGEMENTS

Financial support for this work and permission to publish from the UK Department of Energy is gratefully acknowledged. The opinions expressed in this paper are, however, those of the authors and should not in any way be construed as representing the position or opinions of the Department of Energy.

The major contribution made by Mr P.G. Walton in performing much of the detailed rope examination and testing whilst working at Reading is acknowledged. Acknowledgement and thanks is also given to the following companies for providing additional information and facilities: British Ropes Ltd, BP Research, BP Central Engineering and Houlder (Offshore) Ltd.

REFERENCES

(1)   Giles, R., Chief Diving Inspector, Department of Energy, Private Communication to A.E. Potts, University of Reading, 11th October 1988.

(2)   British Ropes Ltd., "Fatigue Evaluation of 14mm Diameter High Performance Ropes", Report to Department of Energy, Technical Centre, British Ropes Ltd., March 1987.

(3)   Chaplin, C.R. and Walton, P.G., "Examination of 14mm Multistrand Rope Subjected to Bending-Over-Sheave Fatigue", Report to Department of Energy as part of Project No. 2178, Department of Engineering, University of Reading, March 1987.

(4)   Chaplin, C.R. and others, "Diving Bell Lift Wire Assessment", Report to Department as part of Project No. 2178, Department of Engineering, University of Reading, December 1987.

(5)   DSM 8/1977, "Diving Safety Memorandum No. 8", Department of Energy, Petroleum Engineering Division, 9th May, 1977.

(6)   DSM 5/1982, "Diving Safety Memorandum No. 5/1982 - Safety Apparatus/ Lifting Equipment, Health and Safety During Operations at Work Regulations 1982", Department of Energy Petroleum Engineering Division, 8th March 1982.

(7)   DSM 17/1982, "Diving Safety Memorandum No. 17/1982 - Examination and Testing of Lifting Equipment, Health and Safety Diving Operations at Work Regulations 1981", Department of Energy Petroleum Engineering Division, 24th August 1982.

(8)   ISO 4301 - 1980, "Lifting Appliances - Classification." International Standards Organisation, 1980.

(9)   ISO 4308 - 1981, "Cranes - Selection of Wire Ropes." International Standards Organisation, 1981.

(10)   SI No. 399, "Health and Safety Act - Diving Operations at Work Regulations - Part 13. Maintenance, Examination and Testing of Plant and Equipment", Statutory Instruments No. 399, HMSO, 1st July 1981.

(11)   Lloyd's Register of Shipping, "Code for Lifting Appliances in a Marine Environment", Lloyd's Register of Shipping, London, January 1987.

(12)   British Ropes Ltd., "Guidance Notes - Socketing, Installation and
         Maintenance of Diving Bell Hoist Ropes", 4th Draft, Recommended Guidance
         Notes to the Department of Energy Diving Inspectorate, British Ropes Ltd.,
         November 1986.

(13)   ISO 4309 - 1981, "Wire Ropes for Lifting Appliances - Code of Practice for
         Examination and Discard", International Standards Organisation, 1981.

(14)   BS 6570:1986, "Code of Practice for the Selection, Care and Maintenance of
         Steel Wire Ropes", British Standards Institution, 1986.

(15)   Robertson, D.H., MaTSU, Department of Energy, Private Communication to
         C.R. Chaplin, University of Reading, 19th November 1987.

(16)   NCB "Ropeman's Handbook", National Coal Board, Mining Department,
         Third Edition, 1980.

(17)   BS 443:1982, "Specification for Testing Zinc Coatings on Steel Wire and
         Quality Requirements", British Standards Institution, 1982.

(18)   BS 2763:1982, "Specification for Round Carbon Steel Wire for Wire Ropes",
         British Standards Institution, 1982.

(19)   ANSI M11.1–1980, "American National Standard for Wire Rope for Mines",
         American National Standards Institute, 1980.

TABLE 1 _Inter-Wire Cross-Over Angles between Strands of Different Lays.

		outer layer			
		RHO	RHL	LHO	LHL
inner layer	RHO	high	low	high	medium
	RHL	low	high	very high	high
	LHO	high	medium	high	low
	LHL	very high	high	low	high

RHO: right hand ordinary lay
RHL: right hand Lang's lay
LHO: left hand ordinary lay
LHL: left hand Lang's lay

TABLE 2 _Visible External Wire Break Discard Criteria Applicable to Multistrand Diving Bell Hoist Ropes

Rope Construction	ISO 4309 - 1981				BS 6570 : 1986
	Ordinary Lay		Lang's Lay		
	6d (1)	30d	6d	30d	10d
17 x 7 FC or WSC 18 x 7 FC or WSC	7	14	3	7	4
17 x 19 FC or WSC (2) 18 x 19 FC or WSC (2) 34 x 19 FC or WSC 36 x 19 FC or WSC	10	19	5	10	8
General	0.08n (3)	0.16n	0.04n	0.08n	

Notes 1: d = nominal diameter of rope

2: Applicable to all comparable compound strand constructions e.g. 17 x 26, 17 x 36 etc.

3: n = number of wires in outer strands

TABLE 3 Summary of BOS Fatigue Tests on 14 mm Multistrand Ropes at FOS = 5 and D/d = 20

Rope Construction	Rope Maker	ISO 4309 Discard Criterion	Cycles Completed for Discard Criterion	BOS cycles to failure	Discard Cycles/ Fatigue Life
Round Wires					
18x7(12/6/FC) RHO	A	7 breaks in 6d	22,781 30,545	33,916 37,869	67% 81%
35x7(16/6+6/6/1) RHO	B	10 breaks in 6d	not detected not detected 37,041	32,970 35,399 43,012	– – 86%
35x7(16/6+6/6/1) RHO	C	10 breaks in 6d	not detected not detected 23,113	14,494 24,266 25,396	– – 91%
Dyeform Wires					
35x7(16/6+6/6/1) RHO	C	10 breaks in 6d	not detected not detected 44,000	38,410 35,769 44,360	– – 99%
35x7(16/6+6/6/1) LHL	C	5 breaks in 6d	not detected not detected 32,200	43,146 34,777 32,902	– – 98%
40x7(18/7+7/7/1) RHO	B	10 breaks in 6d	not detected not detected 18,000	20,739 19,850 18,100	– – 99%

TABLE 4   Summary of Wire Breaks Found in 400 mm Lengths of
Multistrand Ropes

Rope Construction	Rope Maker	Lay Directions Inter-wire Cross-over	Total Number of Wire Breaks at Strand Interfaces
Round Wires			
18x7 RHO	A	RHO/LHL/FC v.high/—	98—59—18
35x7 RHO	B	RHO/LHO/LHL/LH high/low/med.	18—125—4—28
Dyeformed Wires			
35x7 RHO	C	RHO/LHO/LHL/LH high/low/med.	0—122—3—3
35x7 LHL	C	LHL/RHO/RHL/RH med./low/med	0—140—4—9

TABLE 5   Details of Retired Diving Bell Hoist Ropes

	ROPE 1	ROPE 2
Rope Construction	26 mm ø, 35x7 (RHO) dyeformed, gal, 200 grade	30 mm ø, 35x7 (RHO) dyeformed, gal, 200 grade
Service History — number of diving seasons — number of dives — approx. BOS cycles — approx. period in seawater	4 763 15,300 (FoS = 10, D/d = 22) 4,600 hours	3 818 16,400 (FoS = 8, D/d = 21) 5,000 hours
Length Remaining	255 m of original 450 m	250 m of original 440
Maintenance	— end-for-ended during life — tailed and tested annually — frequently relubricated	— tailed after 12 months — proof loaded six monthly — pressure re-lubricated
Rope Breaking Loads (tonnes) — Rated MBL (catalogue val.) — New Test Strength — Used Test Strength	58.7 56.7 59.8 (after 2 years service) Retired: 59.7 & 60.4 (undamaged) 53.6 & 57.7 (damaged)	75.6 70.1 Retired: 71.3 (winch end, uncorroded) 75.9 (mid-length) 79.4 (bell end, corroded)

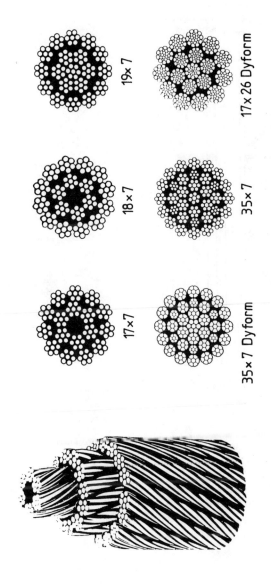

Fig. 1 Cross-Sections of a Number of Multistrand Rope Constructions

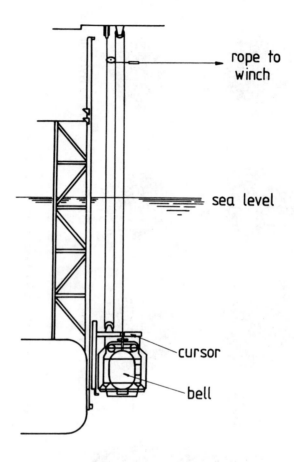

Fig. 2   Diving Bell and Cursor Hoisting Arrangement on one of the Diving Vessels
from which a Retired Hoist Rope was Examined

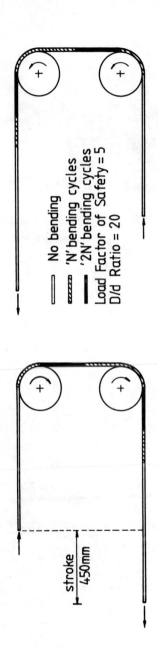

No bending
'N' bending cycles
'2N' bending cycles
Load Factor of Safety = 5
D/d Ratio = 20

stroke
450mm

Fig. 3 Bending-Over-Sheave Fatigue Test Machine Arrangement

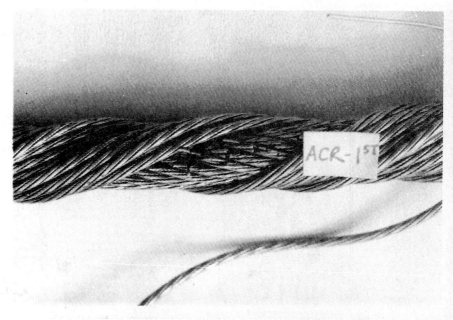

Fig. 4 Outer Strands Removed from a 35 x 7 (LHL) Dyeformed Multistrand Rope
Subject to BOS Fatigue, Showing Typical Internal Break-up on Second Layer

Fig. 5 Damage from Very High Inter-wire Cross-over Angle from 18 x 7 (RHO)
Round Wire Multistrand Rope

Fig. 6 Damage from High Inter-wire Cross-over Angle from 35 x 7 (RHO) Round
Wire Multistrand Rope

Fig. 7 Damage from Medium Inter-wire Cross-over Angle from 35 x 7 (LHL)
Dyeformed Wire Multistrand Rope

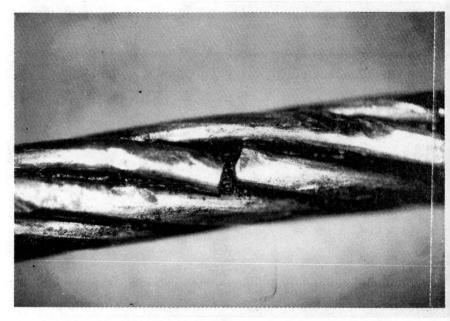

Fig. 8   Damage from Low Inter-wire Cross-over Angle from 35 x 7 (LHL)
Dyeformed Wire Multistrand Rope

Fig. 9   Advanced Internal Fatigue Break-up of a Multistrand Crane Whipline Rope
Removed From Service on an Offshore Platform

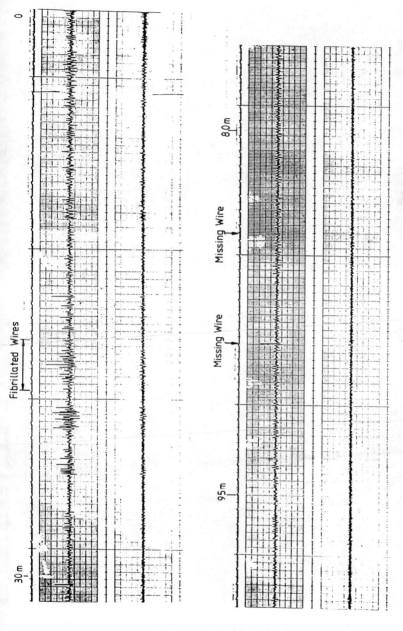

Fig. 10 Condensed NDT Signal Traces from Two Sections of Rope 1, Indicating the Types of Damage Detected

Fig. 11 Fibrillated Outer Wires Due to Multi-layer Winding on the Winch

Fig. 12 Isolated Missing Outer Wire Detected With the NDT Equipment

WIRE ROPE NDT BIBLIOGRAPHY

Compiled by
A.E. POTTS AND S.D. POTTS

The development of non-destructive testing techniques for steel wire ropes goes back to the start of this century, with work on AC electromagnetic NDT devices. Since then a large number of patents have been issued for various devices and much has been published on wire rope NDT, particularly electromagnetic techniques. The development and application of NDT techniques and equipment has taken place in a number of countries, most notably Poland, Germany, Canada, USA, South Africa and Australia. Unfortunately there has been no particular forum or learned society to act as a focus for this work and as a result details and findings are published in a many different journals and conference proceedings, and in many languages. This bibliography is an attempt to draw together this diaspora of published information on the subject. Only the English titles to the references published in other languages have been provided, where translations have been made a reference to it is included.

The bibliography includes some 267 references and has been divided into four sections:
  (i)   General NDT Reviews (4 No.);
  (ii)   Acoustic Emission (23 No.);
  (iii) Electromagnetic Methods (232 No.); and,
  (iv)   Vibro-Acoustic Methods (8 No.).

A large number of these references have been collected by the Rope Research Group in the Department of Engineering at the University of Reading, and many titles were sourced from the list of references in these papers and reports. Dr. N.F. Casey at the National Engineering Laboratory (NEL), East Kilbride, provided additional titles relating to acoustic emission techniques for wire ropes. Dr. C.H.H. Corden provided a comprehensive list of some 140 references, including all the listed translations, on wire rope NDT held at the Health and Safety Executive, Research and Laboratory Services Division, Sheffield. These contributions are gratefully acknowledged.

This bibliography is extensive but by no means complete. Apologies are made to authors and institutions whose papers and reports have not been included. It is believed that no similar bibliography on this subject has been compiled or published previously, so it is hoped that this will form a solid foundation for any up-dated and improved versions to be issued in the future.

Department of Engineering, University of Reading,
Whiteknights, P.O.Box 225, Reading, Berkshire, RG6 2AY, UK.

General NDT Reviews

1. Babel, H. "Destructive and Non-Destructive Test Methods to Determine the Life of Wire Ropes - Part I". Wire, Vol. 28, No. 6, 1979, pp. 38-44.

2. Babel, H. "Destructive and Non-Destructive Test Methods to Determine the Life of Wire Ropes - Part II". Wire, Vol. 29, No. 1, 1980, pp. 263-270.

3. Chaplin, C.R. & Potts, A.E., "Wire Rope in Offshore Applications". MTD, London, February 1988.

4. Corden, C.H.H., "A Review of Wire Rope Non-Destructive Testing and its Practical Application". Proc. Symposium on the Non-Destructive Testing of Steel Wire Ropes held at Inst. of Metals on 6 December, 1988, B. Inst. NDT, February 1989.

Acoustic Emission

1. Bamberger, Y. & Robert, J.L., "Acoustic Testing of Cables", Proc. 1st European Conference on Non-Destructive Testing, Mainz, Germany, Vol. 2, 24-26 April, 1978, pp 355-360.

2. Casey, N.F., "The Evaluation of Wire Ropes by Acoustic Emission and Other Techniques, PhD Thesis, University College Cardiff, 1984.

3. Casey, N.F., & Taylor, J.L., "The Acoustic Emission of Steel Wire Ropes", Wire Industry, Vol. 51, No. 601, January 1984, pp 79-82.

4. Casey, N.F. & others, "The Acoustic Detection of the Failure of Constituent Wires of Wire Rope", Wire Industry, Vol. 52, No. 617, May 1985, pp 307-309.

5. Casey, N.F. & others, "The Acoustic Emission Inspection of Wire Rope", OIPEEC Round Table Conference, Glasgow, June 1985, pp. 3.2.1-3.2.18.

6. Casey, N.F. & Taylor, J.L., "The Evaluation of Wire Ropes by Acoustic Emission Techniques", British Journal of Non-Destructive Testing, November 1985, pp. 351-356.

7. Casey, N.F. & others, "Frequency Analysis of the Signals Generated by the Failure of Constituent Wires of Wire Rope", NDT International, Vol. 18, No. 6, December 1985, pp 339-344.

8. Casey, N.F. & Taylor, J.L., "An Instrument for the Evaluation of Wire Ropes: A Progress Report", British Journal of Non-Destructive Testing, January, 1987, pp. 18-21.

9. Casey, N.F. & others, "The Acoustic Evaluation of Wire Ropes Immersed in Water", NDT International, Vol. 20, No. 3, June 1987, pp. 173-176.

10. Casey, N.F. & others, "Wire Break Detection During the Tensile Fatigue Testing of 40mm Diameter Wire Rope", British Journal of Non-Destructive Testing, Vol. 30, No. 5, September 1988, pp 338-341.

11. Casey, N.F., "The Acoustic Emission of Wire Rope", Proc. Symposium on the Non-Destructive Testing of Steel Wire Ropes held at Inst. of Metals on 6 December, 1988, B. Inst. NDT, February 1989.

12. Fritz, J.T.D. & others, "Experimental Development of a Wire Rope Monitoring Device for Laboratory Fatigue Testing", Report ME 1593, for Haggie Rand Ltd., Mine Equipment Research Unit, CSIR, Pretoria, South Africa, September 1978.

13. Hanzawa, M. & others, "Fatigue Behaviour of Large-Diameter Wire Ropes", Society of Petroleum Engineers Journal, Vol. 23, No. 3, June 1982.

14. Hanzawa, M. & others, "Fatigue Behaviour of Large-Diameter Wire Ropes", Proc. 13th Annual OTC, Paper No. OTC 3999, Houston, Texas, May 1981.

15. Harris, D.O. & Dunegan, H.L., "Acoustic Emission Testing of Wire Rope", Materials Evaluation, Vol. 32, No. 1, January 1974, pp 1-6.

16. Holford, K.M., "Non-Destructive Testing of Wire Ropes by Acoustic Emission", PhD Thesis, University College, Cardiff, 1987.

17. Laura, P.A. & others, "Acoustic Detection of Structural Failure of Mechanical Cables", Journal of the Acoustical Society of America, Vol. 45, No. 3, March 1969, pp 791-793.

18. Laura, P.A. & others, "Mechanical Behaviour of Stranded Wire Rope and Feasibility of Detection of Cable Failure", Marine Technology Society Journal, Vol. 4, No. 3, May-June 1970, pp 19-32.

19. Matthews, J.R. & Black, M.R., "Acoustic Emission Signature of Variable Depth Sonar Tow Cable, International Advances in Non-Destructive Testing, Vol. 7, 1981, pp 181-214.

20. Matthews, J.R. & others, "Cable Integrity by Acoustic Emission", US Patent No. 4,565,964, January 1986.

21. Taylor, J.L. & Casey, N.F., "The Acoustic Emission of Steel Wire Ropes", Wire Industry, January 1984, pp. 79-82.

22. Toda, Y. & others, "Detection of Wire Breakage During Tensile Fatigue Tests of Wire Rope", Proc. 10th World Conference on Non-Destructive Testing, Moscow, August 22-28, 1982, pp. 174-181.

23. Torangi Sarjamee, S.Z. & Taylor, J.L., "Aspects of Acoustic Emission of Wire Ropes", Final Project Report, SERC/MTD Managed Programme on The Behaviour of Wire Ropes in Offshore Applications, University College, Cardiff, June 1987.

Electro-magnetic Methods

1. Aimone, P., "Non-Destructive Testing of Wire Ropes in the Mining Industry", Proc. 85th Annual General Meeting of the Canadian Institute of Mining (CIM), Paper No. 66, 1983.

2. Anderson, C., "Detailed Magnetic Profiles Over an Electro-magnetic Conductor", Canadian Mining Journal, Vol. 95, No. 10, October 1974.

3. Ardouin, J. "The Development of Electromagnetic Methods for Inspecting Cableway Ropes", Apave, Vol. 55, 1974.

4. Arnold, H., "Suspended Monorail Trains and Trains Using Floor-Mounted Tracks", Glückauf, Vol. 110, No. 11, (SMRE Translation 6440), June 1974, pp. 435-438.

5. Arnold, H., "New Methods of Testing and Investigating Highly-Stressed Shaft Winding and Cable-Belt Roadway Conveyor Installations", Proc. 16th International Conference of Coal Mine Safety Research, Washington D.C., September 1975.

6. Arnold, H., "Testing and Examination of Deep and Highly Stressed Winding Ropes", Glückauf, Vol. 112, No. 225, 1976, pp. 1263-1268.

7. Arnold, H., "Magnetic-induction Wire Testing; a Facility for Monitoring Installations and Plants Having Movable and Fixed Rope Systems", Standing Committee for Operational Safety and Health in Bituminous Coal Mines, Doc. No. 3823/16, (SMRE Translation 7015), Luxembourg, October 1976.

8. Arnold, H., "Electro-magnetic Testing of Wire Ropes – An Aid to the Surveillance of Installations and Structures with Moving or Stationary Rope Systems", Mines Safety and Health Commission, Doc. No. 38323/76, Luxembourg, October 1976.

9. Arnold, H., "Electro-magnetic Testing of Wire Ropes – An Aid to the Surveillance of Installations and Structures with Moving or Stationary Rope Systems", Der Stahlbau, No. 8, 1977, pp 234-240.

10. Barrett, C.M., "Non-Destructive Testing of Mine Hoisting Ropes in Ontario", Ontario Department of Mines, July 1964.

11. Bavins, T., "Non-Destructive Testing of Semi-Submersible Production Platform Moorings", Proc. Symposium on the Non-Destructive Testing of Steel Wire Ropes held at Inst. of Metals on 6 December, 1988, B. Inst. NDT, February 1989.

12. Beissner, R.E. & others, "NDE Application of Magnetic Leakage Field Methods: A State-of-the-Art Survey", Southwest Research Institute, San Antonio, Texas, January 1980.

13. Belyi, V.D. & Treiger, M.B., " Electromagnetic Counter of Broken Wires In Mine Ropes", Collection of Scientific Papers, MakNII, Vol. 14, 1960, pp. 16–20.

14. Belyi, V.D. & Treiger, M.B., "Theoretical and Experimental Investigations into the Pick-up Unit of a Defectoscope for Ropes of a Sealed-in Type", Vaprosy Gornsi Elektromekaniki, (LTS Translation 3962), Vol. 5, 1962, pp. 88-99.

15. Berezhinsky, V.I. & Prikhod'ko, V.M., "Electro-magnetic Testing of Winding Ropes in the USSR", Mines Safety Conference Karlovy Vary, (NCB Translation M20817/JG), Czechoslovakia, 21 October 1973.

16. Berezhinsky, V.I., "Quantitative Foundation of Rope Discarding Norms with Instrumental Non-Destructive Control", Proc. 1st International Symposium on Non-Destructive Testing of Steel Ropes, Kraków, Poland, 1974, pp. 5-14.

17. Berezhinsky, V.I., "Control of Steel Rope Operation", Bezopasnost Truda v Promyshenosti, No. 11, November 1981, pp. 36-38.

18. Bergander, M.J., "Principles of Magnetic Detectoscopy of Steel Ropes", Presented at 47th Annual Convention of the Wire Association, Boston, November 1977, Published Wire Journal, May 1978.

19. Bergander, M.J., "Magnetic Flux Leakage Inspection of Wire Rope", Int. Advances in Non-Destructive Testing, Vol. 9, 1983, pp. 113-123.

20. Bohr- und Schrämkronenfabrik, "Device for Testing Haulage Ropes", German Patent 257 843 Kl. 42k Gr. 21, 1913.

21. Burgun, A., "Operational Checking of Winding Ropes", Industrie Minerale, (MRDE/NCB Translation 1240), Part 4-79, 1979, pp 227-244.

22. Butler, R. & Higginson, N., "Non-Destructive Examination of Steel Wire Ropes", Safety in Mines Research Advisory Board (Internal Report), Paper No. 4 (69), 1969.

23. Cavanagh, P.E. & Segsworth, R.S., "Non-Destructive Inspection of Mine Hoist Cable", A.S.M. Transations, Vol. 37, 1947.

24. Cavanagh, P.E., "Some Changes in Physical Properties of Steels and Wire Rope During Fatigue Failure", C.I.M. N.I.E. Bulletin, July 1947.

25. Cavanagh, P.E., "The Progress of Failure in Metals as Traced by Changes in Magnetic and Electrical Properties", A.S.T.M. Transations, 1947.

26. CEGB, "Detecting Corrosion of Overhead Lines", Achievements in Technological Planning and Research, Central Electricity Generating Board, 1983/84.

27. Cesnek, V. & Boroska, J., "Defectoscopic Testing of Steel Ropes and a Comparison of the Results of the Tests Obtained with Different Magnetic Defectoscopes", Proc. 1st International Symposium on Non-Destructive Testing of Steel Ropes, Kraków, Poland, June 1974, pp. 15-24.

28. Cholewa, W. & Hansel, J., "The Use of Magnetic Testing Results for the Model Construction of the Weakening of Wire Ropes", OIPEEC, Round Table Conference, Kraków, Poland, June 1981, pp. 95-104.

29. Corden, C.H.H., "Magnetic Non-Destructive Testing of Wire Ropes", Safety in Mines Research Advisory Board (Internal Report), Paper No. 5 (69), 1969.

30. Corden, C.H.H., "Non-Destructive Examination of Wire Ropes: A Progress Report on an Assessment of the MD-6 Defectograph and Future Trends in This Field", Safety in Mines Research Advisory Board (Internal Report), Paper No. 3 (73), 1973.

31. Corden, C.H.H., "Non-Destructive Testing of Wire Rope – Tests on the Performance of Seven Instruments, Mainly on Locked Coil Mining Ropes", Report for the European Community, Mines Safety and Health Commission, 1979 (released for publication 1989).

32. Cosby, J.R. & others, "Detection Instrumentation for Cable Shield Defects", US Bureau of Mines, CFR 33-81, (NTIS, PB 81-194540), 29 August, 1980, p. 50.

33. Coultate, A.K., "Non-Destructive Testing of Mine Haulage Ropes", Proc. of the International Conference on Non-Destructive Testing (Eurotest Conf. on New Trends in NDT), paper No. VI-8, Brussels, 24-26 March 1982.

34. Coultate, A.K., "Non-Destructive Testing of Wire Ropes within British Coal", Proc. Symposium on the Non-Destructive Testing of Steel Wire Ropes held at Inst. of Metals on 6 December, 1988, B. Inst. NDT, February 1989.

35. CSIR, "Survey of Methods of Non-Destructive Testing of Winder Ropes in South Africa", Report MEG 880, for the Chamber of Mines of South Africa, Mine Equipment Research Unit, CSIR, Pretoria, South Africa, March 1970.

36. CSIR, "The Interpretation of Test Traces Obtained with South African AC-Electro-magnetic Instrument on Winder Ropes", Report MEG 893, for the Chamber of Mines of South Africa, Mine Equipment Research Unit, CSIR, Pretoria, South Africa, April 1970.

37. CSIR, "Comparison Tests of Electro-magnetic Instruments in Use in South Africa for the Non-Destructive Testing of Wire Ropes. Part I – Field and Laboratory Tests", Report MEG 934, for the Chamber of Mines of South Africa, Mine Equipment Research Unit, CSIR, Pretoria, South Africa, August 1970.

38. CSIR, "Comparison Tests of Electro-magnetic Instruments in Use in South Africa for the Non-Destructive Testing of Wire Ropes. Part II – Appendices", Report MEG 935, for the Chamber of Mines of South Africa, Mine Equipment Research Unit, CSIR, Pretoria, South Africa, August 1970.

39. Davis, B., "Progress Report of Electro-magnetic Tests Made on Mine Hoist Ropes in Ontario", The Canadian Mining and Metallurgical Bulletin, January 1963, pp. 12-14.

40. Di Santolo, D., "A Miniature Magnetic-Inductive Instrument for Inspecting Ropes While in Service on Ropeways", Lift, March/April, 1973.

41. Egen, R.A. & Benson, D.K., "Wire Rope Retirement Criteria and Procedures", Progress Report No. 16, US Bureau of Mines, Contract No. JO155187, Midwest Research Institute Kansas City, November 1976.

42. Egen, R.A., "Non-Destructive Testing of Wire Rope", Proc. 9th Annual OTC, Paper No. OTC 2926, Houston, Texas, May 1977, pp. 375-382.

43. Ellis, O.W., "The Application of the Cyctograph to Non-Destructive Inspection of Materials, in Particular, Wire Ropes", Wire & Wire Products, October 1946.

44. Ellis, O.W. & others, "Most Recent Developments in Rope Testing at the Ontario Research Foundation", Canadian Mining and Metallurgy Bulletin 47, March 1954.

45. Federal Office of Transport, "Magneto-Inductive Rope Inspection in Practice", Proc. International Congress of Transportation by Rope, Paper No. 2, Luzern, July 1969.

46. Finkelstein, L. & Hardwick, I.R., "The Detection of Flaws and Weaknesses in Wire Ropes", National Coal Board, Mining Research Establishment, Technical Memo. No. 1, January 1956.

47. Foerster, F., "Theoretical and Experimental Developments in Magnetic Stray Flux Techniques for Defect Detection", British Journal of Non-Destructive Testing, November 1975, pp. 168-171.

48. Forster, F., "New Findings in the Field of Non-Destructive Magnetic Leakage Field Inspection", NDT International, Vol. 19, No. 1, February 1986, pp. 3-14.

49. Förster, F., "Theoretical and Experimental Foundation of Non-Destructive Testing Using Eddy Current. Part I – Test Coil Methods", Zeitschrift Metallkunde, Vol. 43, No. 5, 1952, pp. 163-171.

50. Förster, F. & Breitfeld, H., "Non-Destructive Testing Using Eddy Current Methods. Part II – Practical Results and Industrial Applications of Methods Using Test Coils", Zeitschrift Metallkunde, Vol. 43, No. 5, 1952, pp. 172–180.

51. Förster, F. & Stambke, K., "Non-Destructive Testing Using Eddy Current Methods. Part III – Quantitative Methods of Non-Destructive Testing Using Test Object Encircling Coils", Zeitschrift Metallkunde, Vol. 45, No. 4, 1954, pp. 166-179.

52. Förster, F., "Theoretical and Experimental Foundation of Non-Destructive Testing Using Eddy Current. Part IV – Practical Apparatus for NDT Using Encircling Coils for Eddy Currents", Zeitschrift Metallkunde, Vol. 45, No. 4, 1954, pp. 180-187.

53. Förster, F. & Breitfeld, H., "Theoretical and Experimental Foundation of Non-Destructive Testing Using Eddy Current. Part V – Practical Apparatus for NDT Using Encircling Coils for Eddy Currents", Zeitschrift Metallkunde, Vol. 45, No. 4, 1954, pp. 188-199.

54. Frenkiel, Z., "First International Symposium in Kraków on Non-Destructive Testing of Steel Wire Ropes", Lift, Vol. 16, part 4, July/August 1974, pp. 118–120.

55. Frenkiel, Z., "More About Technical Investigations of Wire Ropes", Wire Industry, November 1976.

56. Füchs, D. & Schröder, R., "New Developments in and Applications of Wire Rope Testing Equipment from WBK-Seilprüfstelle", Proc. Symposium on the Non-Destructive Testing of Steel Wire Ropes held at Inst. of Metals on 6 December, 1988, B. Inst. NDT, February 1989.

57. Grupe, H., "Development of Apparatus for Examining Hoisting Ropes by the Magnetic Induction Process", Research Report for the State of Nordrhein-Westfalen, No. 954, Westdeutscher Verlag, Köln-Opladen, 1961.

58. Grupe, H., "Magneto-Inductive Test Equipment for Steel Wire Ropes", Glückhauf, Vol. 110, No. 23, December 1974, pp. 993-995.

59. Grupe, H., "Use of Hall Generators With Magnetic Induction Rope Testing Equipment", Mines Safety and Health Commission, Doc. No. 5210/79e, Luxemburg, October 1979.

60. Hackenberg, W., "Methods of Monitoring Ropes in Mine Hoists", Glückhauf, Vol. 115, No. 18, 1979, pp. 902 904.

61. Haibach, E. & others, "Principles, Possibilities and Limits of Magnetic Testing of Steel Wire Ropes", OIPEEC Bulletin 46, November 1983.

62. Hanke, E. & Plickat, F., "Electro-magnetic Testing of Steel Wire Ropes for Damage and Corrosion", Mitteilung aus dem Institut für Werkstoffkunde und zerstorungsfreie Werkstoffprufung, Magdeburg, DDR, 1959.

63. Hansel, J, "Some Works on Fatigue Life and Reliability Diagnostic of Wire Rope", OIPEEC Bulletin 47, 1984, pp. 9-31.

64. Hansel, J., "Results of Some Selected Works on Shaft Hoisting at the University of Mining and Metallurgy in Kraköw", Kwartalnik "Mechanika", Publ. AGH, Kraköw, Poland, Vol. 4, 1985, pp. 5-30.

65. Hansel, J., "Rubber Coated Flat Tail Ropes for Mine Hoists", International Conference on Hoisting of Men, Materials and Minerals, The Canadian Institute of Mining and Minerals, Toronto, 1988, Vol. 2, pp. 1115-1131.

66. Hansel, J., & Lankosz, L., "Magnetic Testing of Winding Ropes", International Conference on Hoisting of Men, Materials and Minerals, The Canadian Institute of Mining and Minerals Toronto, 1988, Vol. 2, pp. 1285-1294.

67. Hansel, J., & Cholewa, W., "Determination of Wear of Wire Ropes Operating in Sea Water Conditions", Morski Instytut Rybacki, Gdynia, 1980, pp 195-207.

68. Hansel, J. & others, "Non-Destructive Testing of Wire Ropes on Surface Mining Equipment", The International Journal of Exploring, Developing, Operating, Managing Surface Mines, Trans Tech Publications 1-3, 1987, pp. 277-281.

69. Hansel, J. & others, "Problems of the Quantitative Assessment of Properties of Wires and Wire Ropes", Mechanizacja i Automatyzacja Górnictwa Nr.3-4, Katowice 1987.

70. Hansel, J. & others, "Wire Rope Non-Destructive Testing in Poland - Equipment, Methods of Testing and Statutory Regulations", Proc. Symposium on the Non-Destructive Testing of Steel Wire Ropes held at Inst. of Metals on 6 December, 1988, B. Inst. NDT, February 1989.

71. Harvey, T. & Krüger, H.W., "The Theory and Practice of Electronic Testing of Winding Ropes", Trans. of SA Inst. Elect. Engineers, Vol. 5 part 6, June 1959, pp. 126-181.

72. Harvey, T., "Electronic Testing of Winding Ropes in the Mining Industry in South Africa", Proc. 8th Commonwealth Mining and Metallurgical Congress, Vol. 6, 1965.

73. Haynes, H.H. & Underbakke, L.D., "Non-Destructive Test Equipment for Wire Rope", Technical Note N-1594, Naval Civil Engineering Laboratory, Port Hueneme, Calif., October 1980.

74. HSE, "Non-Destructive Examination of Wire Ropes", Technical Information Leaflet, Engineering and Metallurgy No. 1.

75. Hill, D.A. & Wait, J.R., "Analysis of Alternating Current Excitation of a Wire Rope by a Toroidal Coil", J. Applied Physics, Vol. 48, No. 12, December 1977.

76. Hill, D.A. & Wait, J.R., "Scattering by a Slender Void in a Homogeneous Conducting Wire Rope", J. Applied Physics, Vol. 16, 1978, pp. 391-398.

77. Hill, D.A. & Wait, J.R., "Electromagnetic Field Perturbation by an Internal Void in a Conducting Cylinder Excited by a Wire Loop", J. Applied Physics, Vol. 18, 1979, pp. 141-147.

78. Hill, D.A. & Wait, J.R., "Dynamic Electro-magnetic Response of a Homogeneous Conducting Cylinder for Symmetric Excitation", J. Applied Physics, Vol. 20, 1979, pp. 89-96.

79. Hill, D.A. & Wait, J.R., "Electro-magnetic Interaction Between a Conducting Cylinder and a Solenoid in Relative Motion", J. Applied Physics, Vol. 50, No. 8, August 1979.

80. Hill, D.A. & Wait, J.R., "Theory of Electro-magnetic Methods for Non-Destructive Testing of Wire Ropes", Report No. 80303, US Dept. of Commerce, Boulder, Colorado, 1980.

81. Hiltbrunner, R.H., "The Magnetic Inspection of Ropes with the Defectoscope Integra", Economie Tech. Transports, No. 119, June 1957.

82. Hindson, J.A., "A.C. Electro-magnetic Testing of Winding Ropes on the Mines in Zambia", J. of Engineering Inst. of Zambia, Vol. 12, No. 1, February 1968.

83. Hirama, Y & others, "Electro-magnetic Inspecting Apparatus for Magnetizable Wire Rope", U.S. Patent No. 4,427,904, 24 January 1984.

84. Hitchen, H., "Non-Destructive Methods of Testing Wire Ropes for Mining Operations", British Ropes Ltd., Doncaster, Pub. No. 263, Reprinted from "Mining Equipment", September 1960.

85. Jasiewicz, W. & Lankosz, L., "Use of Defectoscopes for Wire Rope Inspections", OIPEEC, Round Table Conference, Kraków, Poland, June 1981, pp. 105-110.

86. Jezewski, M. & others, "New Improvements of Magnetic Wire Ropes Testing Method", Biuletyn PAU, Vol. 1, Kraków, 1951.

87. Jezewski, M. & Kawecki, Z., "Theory and Practice with the Electro-magnetic Rope Testing Process", Glückauf, Vol. 95, No. 17, (LTS 3023), August 1959, pp. 1067-1074.

88. Jezewski, M.S. & others, "Magnetic Device for Determining Defects in Rod-Like Elements, Cables, Steel Pipes and the Like", US Patent No. 3,424,967, 28 January 1969.

89. Kalwa, E., "Detection and Measurement of Faults in Steel Cable by Magnetic Testing Method", Doctoral Dissertation, University of Mining and Metallurgy, Kraków, Poland, December 1982.

90. Kalwa, E. & Piekarski, K., "Detection of Defects in a Steel Rope with the Hall-Effect Magnetic Probe", Can. Soc. of N.D.T. Journal, Vol. 7, No. 4, July-August 1986, pp. 40-45.

91. Kalwa, E. & Piekarski, K., "Fundamentals of Magnetic Tesing of Steel Wire Rope", Can .Soc. of N.D.T. Journal, Vol. 8, No. 1, January-February 1987, pp. 36-43.

92. Kalwa, E. & Piekarski, K., "Abrasion of Wire Ropes – Their Models and the Magnetic Testing Method", Can. Soc. of N.D.T. Journal, Vol. 8 No. 2, March-April 1987, pp. 46-49.

93. Kalwa, E. & Piekarski, K., "Magnetic Testing of Steel Ropes", Proc. of Fifth Pan Pacific Conf. on NDT, Vancouver, April 1987.

94. Kalwa, E. & Piekarski, K., "Design of Hall-Effect Sensors for Magnetic Testing of Steel Ropes", NDT International, Vol. 20, No. 5, October 1987, pp. 295-301.

95. Kalwa, E. & Piekarski, K., "Design of Inductive Sensors for Magnetic Testing of Steel Ropes", NDT International, Vol. 20, No. 6, December 1987, pp. 347-353.

96. Kalwa, E. & Piekarski, K., "Determination of Flaws Located at Different Depth Levels in the Cross-Section of Steel Rope", NDT International, Vol. 21, No. 2, April 1988, pp. 77-82.

97. Kalwa, E. & Piekarski, K., "Qualitative and Quantitative Determination of Densely Occurring Defects in Steel Ropes by Magnetic Testing Method", American Soc. for NDT, Materials Evaluation, Vol. 46, May 1988, pp. 767–770.

98. Kappelhof, M.C., "Electro-magnetic Examination and Endurance Testing of Lock Coil Winding Ropes", Doctoral Thesis, Technical University of Delft, April 1973.

99. Kappelhof, M.C., "Electro-magnetic Examination and Endurance Testing of Lock Coil Winding Ropes", OIPEEC Round Table Conference, Milan, September 1973.

100. Kappelhof, M.C., "Electro-magnetic Examination and Endurance Testing of Lock Coil Winding Ropes", Proc. 1st International Symposium on Non-Destructive Testing of Steel Ropes, Kraków, June 1974.

101. Kastner, J., "Improved Rope Testing", Draht, Vol. 18, No. 8, 1967.

102. Kawecki, Z., "A Few Considerations About the Testing of Rope-Railway and Mine-Winding Ropes with the Polish Electro-magnetic Defectoscope", Joint Conference on Metallic Studies and Mining Machinery, Freiberg, (LTS Translation 3231), July 1959.

103. Kawecki, Z., & Stachurski, J., "Report about the State of Investigation in the Field of Steel Ropes", International Organisation of Rope Transport (OITAF), 1979.

104. Kawecki, Z., "Some Problems of Quantitative Evaluation of Indications Obtained by Means of the Electro-magnetic Inspection of Wire Ropes", International Ropeway Review, Part I, Vol. 5, July-September 1963.

105. Kawecki, Z., "Some Problems of Quantitative Evaluation of Indications Obtained by Means of the Electro-magnetic Inspection of Wire Ropes", International Ropeway Review, Part II, Vol. 5, October-December 1963.

106. Kawecki, Z. & others, "Defining the Permissible Operation Time of a Steel Rope on the Ground of Periodic Magnetic Inspections", Scientific Publ. on Electrification and Mechanisation of Mines of the University of Mining and Metallurgy, Kraków, No. 16, 1966.

107. Kawecki, Z. & Stachurski, J., "Magnetic Defectoscopy of Steel Ropes", publ. Slask, Katowice, Poland, 1969.

108. Kawecki, Z. & others, "The Development of the Apparatus for the Magnetic Testing of Steel Ropes Devised at the Academy of Mining and Metallurgy of Kraków", Proc. 7th Int. Conf. on NDT, Paper No. D-33, Warsaw , June 1973.

109. Kawecki, Z. & Stachurski, J., "Trends of the Investigations of the Development of Magnetic Testing of Steel Ropes Carried Out at the St. Staszic University of Mining and Metallurgy in Kraków", Proc. 1st International Symposium on Non-Destructive Testing of Steel Ropes, Kraków, Poland, June 1974.

110. Kawecki, Z. & Hansel, J., "Development and Future Perspective of the Magnetic Testing of Steel Wire Ropes", Internationales Colloquium: 150 Jahre Drahtseil, Technische Akademie, Esslingen, 1984.

111. Kawecki, Z. & Lunkosz, L., "Selected Problems of the Development of Polish Instruments for Magnetic Defectoscopy of Wire Ropes", Kwartalnik "Mechanika" publ. AGH books, Vol. 4, No. 2, 1985.

112. Kibinski, J. & Stachurski, J., "Universal Magnetic Defectograph for Testing Steel Ropes", Problems of Technical Progress, No. 1, Katowice, 1967.

113. Kitzinger, F. & Naud, J.R., "New Developments in Electro-magnetic Testing of Wire Rope", Canadian Mining and Metallurgical Bulletin, Vol. 72, No. 806, June 1979, pp. 99-104.

114. Kitzinger, F. & Wint, G.A., "Magnetic Testing Device for Detecting Loss of Metallic Area and Internal and External Defects in Elongated Objects", US Patent No. 4,096,437, 20 June 1978, Canadian Patent No. 1,038,037, 5 September 1978.

115. Kitzinger, F. & Wint, G.A., "Test Results with the Magnograph Wire Rope Tester", Proc. 1st Annual Wire Rope Symposium, March 18-20 1980, Denver Colorado, Publ. Engineering Extension Service, Washington State Univ., 1980.

116. Kokado, J. & others, "Velocity Independent Electro-magnetic Inspection and Other Applications of Magnetogalvanic Semi-conductor on Steel Wire Ropes", Proc. 9th World Conference on NDT, Paper 2A-9, Melbourne, 1979.

117. Kokado, J. & others, "A Speed Independent Electro-magnetic Defect Detector of Steel Ropes", J. Mining and Metallurgical Inst. of Japan (Nippon Kogyo Kaishi), (HSE Trans. No. 8355), Vol. 94, No. 1081 (78-3), March 1978, pp. 157-162.

118. Kruger, H.W., "Recent Developments in the Electro-magnetic Testing of Winding Ropes", Trans. of SA Institute of Electrical Engineers, Vol. 62, Part II, February 1971.

119. Kurz, R., "Magnetic Inductive Testing of Steel Wire Rope", Doctoral Dissertation, München, 1965.

120. Kurz, R., "The Magnetic Induction Method for Cable Testing: Experience and Future Prospects", Proc. 4th International Congress of Transportation by Rope, Vienna, Austria, 1965.

121. Kurz, R., "Magnet-Inductive Wire Rope Testing", Draht-Welt, Vol. 51, No. 12, 1965, pp. 632-638.

122. Kurz, R., "Experiences with Magnet-Inductive Rope Testing", Draht-Welt, Vol. 60, No. 4, 1974, pp. 129-133.

123. Lang, J.G., "Non-Destructive Wire Rope Testing in Ontario", Canadian Mining Journal, Vol. 84, No. 9, September 1963, pp. 60-87.

124. Lang, J.G., "The Principle and Practice of Electro-magnetic Wire Rope Testing", Can. Mining and Metallurgical Bulletin, Vol. 62, No. 684, April 1969, pp. 415-424.

125. Lesin, K.K. & others, "IISK-3 Steel Rope Wear Tester and its Application in the U.S.S.R for Mine Rope Control", Proc. 1st International Symposium on NDT of Steel Ropes, Kraków, Poland, June 1974, pp. 53-58.

126. Lord, W. & Hwang, J.H., "Defect Characterisatin from Magnetic Leakage Fields", British Journal of NDT, January 1977, pp. 14-18.

127. Mackh, H., "Electro-magnetic Testing of Steel Wire Ropes", Arch. fur. Tech. Messen, 5, No. 59, 1936.

128. Maillard, A., "Use of Eddy-Currents for the Non-Destructive Detection and Identification of Steel Rope Defects", Proc. 8th World Conference on NDT, Cannes, France, Paper No. 5B9, September 1976.

129. Marchent, B.G., "Non-Destructive Testing of Wire Ropes", Patent Appl. No. 41530/77, October 1977.

130. Marchent, B.G., "Mooring Cable Non-Destructive Testing", Instrumentation and Comunications IEE Sub-Conference Oceanology International, March 1978, pp. 11-15.

131. Marchent, B.G., "An Instrument for the Non-Destructive Testing of Wire Ropes", Systems Technology, No. 29, August 1978, pp. 26-32.

132. Marchent, B.G., "Aparatus for Non-Destructive Testing of Elongate Objects", U.K. Patent Application GB2, 012, 966A, December 1978.

133. Martyna, R., "Application of Hall Effect Sensors for Detecting Defects on Steel Ropes", Proc. 9th National Conference Paper on NDT, Fromborg, 1979.

134. Martyna, R., "Determination of the Weakening of the Rope by the Magnetic Method with the use of the Digital Defectoscope", Doctoral Dissertation, AGH, Kraków, Poland, 1980.

135. Martyna, R., "Pulse-Digital Testing of Wire Rope Deterioration", OIPEEC Round Table Conference, Kraków, Poland, June 1981, pp. 111-118.

136. Martyna, R., "A Mathematical Model of the Transformation of a Rope Defect into a Magnetic Stray Field", OIPEEC Round Table Conference, Kraków, Poland, June 1981, pp. 119-129.

137. McCann, C.E.S. & Colson, R., "Device for the Determination of Area Loss of Wire Ropes and Cables and Similar Objects", German Patent No. 175,895 Kl. 42b Gr. 10, 1906.

138. McEvoy, S., "The Detection and Classification of Wire and Rod Defects", Wire Industry, December 1981, p. 895.

139. McPhar Manufacturing Ltd., "Dual Frequency Electro-magnetic Rope Tester (O.M.A.)", Mines Safety Commission, Luxembourg, No. 7593-65, October 1965.

140. Mera-Ster, "Magnetic Test Method for Steel Wire Rope Examination", Wire Industry, Vol. 49, No. 8, August 1982, pp. 620-623.

141. Mera-Ster, "Determination of Rope Wear by Magnetic Tests", Wire Industry, February 1985, pp. 113-114.

142. Meyer, U.B., "The Electro-magnetic Testing of Wire Ropes", in Mitteilungen aus dem Institut für Elektrische Maschinen an der ETH, ed. A. Dutoit, Juris Druck und Verlag, Zürich, Switzerland, 1973.

143. Meyer, U.B., "The Electro-magnetic Testing of Wire Ropes", Mitteilungen aus dem Institut für Bau - und Transportmaschinen, August 1973.

144. Meyer, U.B., "The Electro-magnetic Testing of Wire Ropes", VDI-Z, Vol. 116, Part II, 1974.

145. Meyer, U.B., "Electro-magnetic Wire Rope Test" Proc. 1st International Symposium on NDT of Steel Ropes, Kraków, Poland, June 1974, pp. 59-68.

146. Misawa, S. & others, "Flaw Detection in Steel Ropes Using a Hall Generator", Symposium at Faculty of Engineering, Tohoku University, Sendai, Japan, 1964.

147. Mits, V.N., "Experimental Investigation into Magnetic Recording in Steel Hoisting Ropes in Pits", Voprosy Gornoi Electromechaniki, Vol. 5, Moscow, (LTS Translation 3962a), 1962.

148. Mits, V.N., "Theoretical Bases for Increasing the Resolving Power of Magnetic Recording on Steel Ropes", Trudy MakNII, Voprosy Gornoi Elektromekhaniki, Moscow, (SMRE Translation 5320), Vol. 16, 1965, pp. 206-213.

149. Moll, J.H., "Non-destructive Testing of Wire Ropes", Chamber of Mines Journal, May 1972.

150. Morgan, J.P., "Investigations on Wire Ropes in Mine Hoisting System", Proc. Australian Inst. Min. Metall., No. 215, 1965, pp. 59-85.

151. Morgan, J.P., "Search Coils for Non-Destructive Tests on Wire Ropes", Proc. 8th Commonwealth Mining and Metallurgical Congress, Melbourne, ed. J.T. Woodcock & others, Vol. 6, 1965, pp. 1177-1180.

152. Morgan, J.P. & Symes, J.E.J., "Development and Future Significance of Non-Destructive Testing of Winder Ropes", Proc. Australian Inst. Min. Metall, No. 221, 1967, pp. 61-67.

153. Morgan, J.P., "Search-Coil for Non-Destructive Testing of Wire Ropes and Similarly Shaped Objects", Australian Patent No. 278,156 (filed 20 December 1965), (Patent also registered in U.S.A., Canada and Germany), 15 February 1968.

154. Morgan, J.P. & Symes, H.E.J., "Non-Destructive Testing of Wire Ropes", Australian Mineral Industries Research Assoc. Ltd., (AMIRA), Bulletin No. 6, December 1976.

155. NCB, "Non-Destructive Testing of Winding Ropes. A Comparison of Instruments", National Coal Board, Central Engineering Establishment, Test Report LT/MT 497, August 1965.

156. Ontario Mining Association, "Electro-magnetic Rope Tests", Progress Report No. 3, May 1961 - August 1962.

157. OITAF, "Magnetic Inspection of Ropes. Part I", International Ropeway Review, Vol. 9, April-June 1967.

158. OITAF, "Magnetic Inspection of Ropes. Part II", International Ropeway Review, Vol. 9, October-December 1967.

159. OITAF, "Technical Investigations of Wire Ropes", Wire Industry, September 1975.

160. Piao, C.F., & others, "Electro-magnetic Inspection of Steel Wire Rope with Hall Element Detector", J. Min. Metall. Inst. Jpn., 100 (1155), May 1984, pp. 411-415.

161. Plessey, "Wire Haulage Rope Non-Destructive Testing Instruments", Plessey Radar Research Centre, Tech. Note No. 1, 77/N178U, September 1977.

162. Poffenroth, D.N., "Flaw Detection in Mine Hoist Transportation Systems", Proc. 1st Annual Wire Rope Symposium, March 18-20 1980, Denver Colorado, Publ. Engineering Extension Service, Washington State Univ., 1980, pp. 113–138.

163. Poirier, L., "Non-Destructive Testing of Wire Rope", Commission for European Community, Mines Safety and Health Commission, Doc. No. 4278/81, Luxembourg, 1981.

164. Potts, A.E. & Chaplin, C.R., "A Case for Electro-magnetic NDT Inspection of Multistrand Diving Bell Hoist Ropes", Proc. Symposium on the Non-Destructive Testing of Steel Wire Ropes held at Inst. of Metals on 6 December, 1988, B. Inst. NDT, February 1989.

165. Purdie, T.F. & Dent, P.J., "Non-Destructive Testing at Mount Isa Mines Ltd., Australia, with Particular Reference to Koepe Hoist Ropes", Proc. 9th Commonwealth Mining and Metallurgical Congress, 1969.

166. Rieger, W., "A Contribution to the Magnet-Inductive Cross-Sectional Area Measurement of Wire Ropes", Doctoral Dissertation, Universitat Stüttgart, FRG, 1983.

167. Riha, V., "Magnet-Inductive Monitoring of Hoist Ropes", Rudy, 25, 1977.

168. Ross, A.C., "The Use of the Magnetic Defectograph", Can. Mining and Metallurgical Bulletin, Vol. 62, No. 684, April 1969, pp. 425-431.

169. Rotesco Ltd., "D.C. Wire Rope Testing - Elementary Theory and Application", Toronto, Ontario, Canada

170. Rotesco Ltd., "A.C. Wire Rope Testing Techniques - Method and Application", Toronto, Ontario, Canada

171. Roy, P.R. & Tarafder, M.N., "Wire Rope Examination by Non-Destructive Method", Metals and Minerals Review, April 1970.

172. Samarskii, A.F., "Reduction in the Strength of Winding Ropes with Various Types of Deterioration", Trudy MakNII, Voprosy Gornoi Elektromekhaniki, Moscow, Vol. 16, 1965, pp. 286-301.

173. Sandford, R.L. & others, "Effect of Wear on the Magnetic Properties and Tensile Strength of Steel Wire", US Dept. of Commerce, Bureau of Standards, Paper No. 510, 1925.

174. Sandford, R.L., "Non-Destructive Testing of Wire Hoisting Rope by Magnetic Analysis", Technologic Paper No. 315, US National Bureau of Standards, Part of Vol. 20, Govt. Printing Office, Washington, D.C., April 1926.

175. Schleipp, S., "Electro-magnetic Wire Rope Inspection", Doctoral Dissertation, Technische Hochschule Berlin, Berlin, Germany, 1937.

176. Semmelink, A., "Electro-magnetic Testing of Winding Ropes", Trans. of the SA Inst. of Electrical Engineers, Vol. 43, No. 5, May 1953, pp. 113-129.

177. Semmelink, A., "Electro-magnetic Testing of Winding Ropes", Trans. of the SA Inst. of Electrical Engineers, Vol. 44, Part 5, May 1953.

178. Semmelink, A., "Electro-magnetic Testing of Winding Ropes", Trans. of the SA Inst. of Electrical Engineers, Vol. 47, Part 7, July 1956.

179. Seznec, R., "Electro-magnetic Rope Testing", Int. Advances in NDT, Vol. 9, 1983, pp. 124-158.

180. Simpson, W., "Electronic Inspection of Wire Ropes", Paper No. 18, Proc. Conf. on Wire Ropes in Mines, held at Ashorne Hill, Leamington Spa, Warwickshire, September 1950, Inst. of Mining & Metallurgy, 1951, pp. 581-600.

181. Simpson, W., "Electronic Inspection of Wire Ropes While in Service", Discussion on Mine Supports and Wire Ropes. Proc. 7th Int. Conf. of Directors of Safety in Mines Research, Buxton, July 1952. SMRE Res. Rep. No. 66, April 1953.

182. Stachura, J., "Information on Non-Destructive Testing of Hoisting Ropes Carried Out by the District of the Technical Supervision in Katowice for the Needs of the Mining Industry", Proc. 1st Int. Symposium on NDT of Steel Ropes, Kraków, Poland, June 1974, pp. 69-72.

183. Stachurski, J., "The Problem of the Evaluation of Wear Out of Steel Ropes by Means of Magnetic Testing", Scientific Publications AGH, No. 167, Book 20, Kraków, Poland, 1967.

184. Stachurski, J. & Bergander M.J., "Theoretical Approach of Calibration of Defectograph with Integrating Recording", Proc. 1st Int. Symposium on NDT of Steel Ropes, Kraków, Poland, June 1974, pp. 73-88.

185. Stachurski, J., "Magnetic Testing of Steel Wire Ropes", Report from Lab. for Testing Wire Ropes, Univ. of Mining and Metallurgy, Kraków, Poland, 1976.

186. Stachurski, J. & others, "Application of Magnetic Detectors for Continuous Monitoring of Steel Ropes", (HSE Trans. No. 9041), AGH, Kraków, Poland, 1978.

187. Stachurski, J. & others, "Magnetic Testing of Round Mine Haulage Ropes. Determination of Wear Using the Magnetic Method", Polish Code of Practice BN/79/5021/09, (HSE Translation No. 8728), 1979.

188. Stachurski, J. & Bergander, M.J., "The Application of Numerical Methods in Indicating the Extent of Rope Weakenesses on the Basis of Defectograph Readings", (HSE Translation No. 8601), September 1980.

189. Stachurski, J. & others, "Use of Hall-Effect Sensors for Detection of Different Rope Faults", OIPEEC Round Table Conference, Kraków, Poland, June 1981, pp. 137-147.

190. Stachurski, J., "The Influence of the Choice of the Detecting Heads on the Evaluation of Defects of Wire Ropes", OIPEEC Round Table Conference, Kraków, Poland, June 1981, pp. 130-138.

191. Strebelle, J., "Results of Magnetic Tests on Winding Ropes", Trans. No. A1755-FWM, Annales des mines de Belgique, No. 7/8, July-August 1959, pp. 777-784.

192. Swider, W., "Magnetic Test Method for Steel Wire Ropes", British Journal of NDT, March 1983, pp. 72-74.

193. Symes, H.E.J., "Non-Destructive Testing of Winder Ropes", Queensland Govt. Mining Journal, March 1966.

194. Symes, H.E.J., "Magnetic and Eddy Current Testing Methods Applied to Wire Winding Ropes", NDT Association of Australia., Vol. 6, No. 4, 1969, pp. 7-9.

195. Symes, H.E.J., "Electro-magnetic Testing of Mine Winding Ropes - The Field Pattern of an Internal Broken Wire", Ann. Conf. Australian, Inst. Min. & Metall., New Zealand, Paper No. 19, 1971.

196. Symes, H.E.J., "Use, Problems and Non-Destructive Testing of Wire Ropes in Australian Mines", Balgowlah, Australia, June 1975.

197. Symes, H.E.J., "The AMIRA Non-Destructive Wire Rope Tester", NDT - Australia, July 1977.

198. Symes, H.E.J., "The AMIRA Non-Destructive Rope Tester", Australasian Corrosion Engineering, April 1978, pp. 17-19.

199. Tomaiuolo, F.G. & Lang, J.G., "Method and Apparatus for Non-Destructive Testing of Magnetically Permeable Bodies Using a First Flux to Saturate the Body and a Second Flux Opposing the First Flux to Produce a Measurable Flux", US Patent No. 4,495,465, January 1985.

200. Turner, N., "Field Experience in the Non-Destructive Testing of Wire Ropes", Proc. Symposium on the Non-Destructive Testing of Steel Wire Ropes held at Inst. of Metals on 6 December, 1988, B. Inst. NDT, February 1989.

201. Ulrich, E. & Grupe, H., "Inspection of Highly Stressed Mine Hoist Ropes", Glückauf, Vol. 111, No. 18, 1975, pp. 870-874.

202. Underbakke, L.D. & Haynes, H.H., "Test and Evaluation of the Magnograph Unit - a Non-Destructive Wire Rope Tester", TN. No. 1639, Naval Civil Engineering Laboratory, Port Hueneme, Calif. USA, July 1982.

203. Underbakke, L.D., "Test and Evaluation of the MT-75 Wire Rope Tester – a Hand-Held Non-Destructive Wire Rope Testing Device", TN No. 1661, Naval Civil Engineering Laboratory, Port Hueneme, Calif. USA, 1983.

204. Velden, D. van der & Vossen, H.Th., "A Method for the Testing of Steel Wire Ropes by the Electro-magnetic Method", Glückauf, Vol. 92, No. 27-28, 1956, pp. 792-794.

205. Verwilst, J., "Electro-magnetic Checking of Wire Ropes Sponsored by the European Communities", OIPEEC Bulletin No. 34, January 1979, p. 7.

206. Wait, J.R., "Electro-magnetic Induction in an Autostropic Cylinder", Preliminary Report to US Bureau of Mines, Contract No. H0155008, as amended February 1978.

207. Wait, J.R., "The Electro-magnetic Basis for Non-Destructive Testing of Cylindrical Conductors", Preliminary Report to US Bureau of Mines, Contract No. H0155008, March 1978.

208. Wait, J.R. & Gardner, R.L., "Non-Destructive Testing of Cylindrical Conductor with an Internal Anomaly - A Two Dimensional Model", Preliminary Report to US Bureau of Mines, Contract No. H0155008, May 1978.

209. Wait, J.R., "The Electro-magnetic Basis for Non-Destructive Testing of Cylindrical Conductors", IEEE Transactions on Instrumentation and Measurement, Vol. 27, No. 3, September 1978.

210. Wait, J.R., "Electro-magnetic Response of an Ausotropic Conducting Cylinder to an External Source", Radio Science, Vol. 13, No. 5, September-October 1978, pp. 789-792.

211. Wait, J.R. & Gardner, R.L., "Electro-magnetic Non-Destructive Testing of Cylindrically Layered Conductors"", IEEE Transactions on Instrumentation and Measurement, Vol. 28, No. 2, June 1979.

212. Wait, J.R., "Review of Electro-magnetic Methods in Non-Destructive Testing of Wire Ropes", Proceedings of the IEEE, Vol. 67, No. 6, June 1979, pp. 892–903.

213. Wall, T.F., "Electro-magnetic Testing for Mechanical Flaws in Steel Wire Ropes", J. Inst. Elec. Eng., Vol. 67, 1929, pp. 899-911.

214. Wall, T.F. & Hainsworth, C.H., "The Penetration of Alternating Magnetic Flux in Wire Ropes", J. Inst. Elec. Eng., Vol. 71, 1932, pp. 374-379.

215. Wall, T.F., "Electro-magnetic Testing of Wire Ropes", Midland Inst. of Min. Eng., March 1936.

216. Weischedel, H.R., "A Survey of Wire Rope Inspection Procedures", Elevator World, December 1981.

217. Weischedel, H.R., "Magnetic Inspection Device", European Patent Application No. 121,084, February 1984.

218. Weischedel, H.R., "The Inspection of Wire Ropes in Service", Wire Journal International, Vol. 18, No. 9, September 1975, pp. 180-195.

219. Weischedel, H.R., "The Inspection of Wire Ropes in Service: A Critical Review", Materials Evaluation, Vol. 43, No. 13, December 1985, pp. 1592–1605.

220. Weischedel, H.R., "Method and Apparatus for Magnetic Inspection", US Patent No. 4,659,991, 21 April 1987.

221. Weischedel, H.R., "Quantitative In-Service Inspection of Wire Ropes", Materials Evaluation, Vol. 46, No. 4, 1988, pp. 430-437.

222. Wever, F. & Otto, A., "On a Magnetic Method for Testing Wire Ropes, in Particular Haulage Ropes", Mitteilungen aus dem Kaiser-Wilhelm-Institut für Eisenforschung, Düsseldorf, Germany, Vol. 12, 1930, pp. 389-390.

223. Wörnle, R., "Wire Rope Research", Zeitschrift DVI, Vol. 76, 1932, pp. 556–560.

224. Wörnle, R. & Müller, H., "Divided Sense Coil with DC-Driven Device for the Magnetic Testing of Steel Wire Rope", German Patent No. 758,730 Kl. 42k Gr. 4603, 1937.

225. Anon., Apparatus for Detecting Wear in Wire Ropes", Practicing Engineer, 26 July 1907.

226. Anon., "Coming : A New Method to Check Wire Rope", MESA (Magazine of Mining Health and Safety), No. 1, 1976.

227. Anon., "Seminar Group Views Magnetic Wire Rope Tests", MESA (Magazine of Mining Health and Safety), No. 7.

228. Anon., "How Wire Rope Tester Promotes Safety and Increases Service Life", Metal, Mining and Processing, July 1964.

229. Anon, "Electro-magnetic Testing of Winding Ropes", Trans. SA Inst. Electrical Engineers, Vol. 47, No. 8, August 1956, pp. 206-244.

230. Anon., "First International Symposium in Kraköw on Non-Destructive Testing of Steel Wire Ropes", Lift, July/August 1974. Wire Industry, December 1974.

231. Anon., "Determination of Wear by Magnetic Test Method of Steel Wire Ropes for Mine Hoisting", Ministry of Mining, Poland, January 1980.

232. Anon., "Testing Device for Wire Rope", Mining Journal, 2 February 1979.

Vibro-Acoustic

1. Beblo, W. & others, "Prospects for Development of Vibro-Acoustic Methods of Investigation on Properties of Mining Hoist Ropes", OIPEEC Round Table Conference, Kraków, Poland, June 1981, pp. 88-94.

2. Beblo, W. & others, "Prospects for Development of Vibro-Acoustic Methods of Investigation on Properties of Mining Hoist Ropes", Wire Industry, October 1982.

3. Beblo, W. & others, "Towards Evaluation of Progressive Weakening of Hoisting Steel Wire Ropes Using Vibro-Acoustic Methods", Scientific Reviews of the Silesian Polytechnic, No. 589, 1978.

4. dos Reis, H.L.M. & McFarland, D., "On the Acousto-Ultrasonic Non-Destructive Evaluation of Wire Rope Using the Stress Wave Factor Technique", British Journal of NDT, May 1986, pp. 155-156.

5. Hankus, J., "Non-Destructive Tests of a Modulus of Elasticity of the Hoist Rope Under Working Conditions", Proc. 1st International Symposium on NDT of Steel Ropes, Kraków, Poland, June 1974, pp. 89-96.

6. Hochrein, A.A. & others, "Application of Internal Friction Damping as a Non-Destructive Evaluation Technique for Wire Rope", Proc. 15th Annual OTC, Paper No. OTC 4634, May 1983, pp. 447-454.

7. Keyser, D.R. & Mott, G.D., "The Determination of Wire Rope Tension by Frequency Measurement", Proc. 2nd Annual OTC, Paper No. 1296, Vol. II, May 1970, pp. 689-702.

8. Lipowczan, A., "Analysis of Possibilities Related to the Application of Vibro-Acoustic Measuring Methods Aimed at Diagnostics of Hoisting Steel Wire Ropes in Mining", Scientific Reviews of AGH, Kraków, Poland, 1981.